A TREASURY OF PARABLES

A TREASURY OF PARABLES

by

E. J. Bartek

PHILOSOPHICAL LIBRARY

New York

Printed in the United States of America

CONTENTS

INTRODUCTION

Knowledge, as well as wisdom, is a repetition of the same basic principles. It differs only in the relative values of time, place, individual, circumstance, and degree. These basic principles can be a key to the sources of knowledge and of wisdom.

Ever since man began to think he has sought these keys to knowledge. To do this he has integrated facts into unified concepts, and concepts into unified principles and principles into something broader.

This integration toward the unity of knowledge has advanced steadily through the ages. It has been the goal of philosophy. 2500 years ago Plato summed up his wisdom in his "Ideas." He was followed by Aristotle with his "Categories," Thomas Aquinas with his "Summas," Herbert Spencer with his "First Principles," Kant with his "Universals," and Hegel with his "Dialectic Synthesis."

Today we approach unity in the physical sciences with a few unified principles to unite the many laws of physics, chemistry, and astronomy. Einstein's "unified law" of the physical universe is an example. The results of this scientific unity are only too apparent in this electronic, nuclear, and satellite age.

But unity in the science of living things—biology, psychology, sociology—has not been as successful as unity in the non-living sciences. Unitary principles are needed to unify the living sciences and to bridge the gap between spiritual, intellectual, and material knowledge, between theology, philosophy, and science.

We live in an age of increasing specialization. The philosopher, lawyer, and medical doctor, who were well-versed in broad principles, have had their professions disintegrated into hundreds of specialized fields that emphasize detailed facts. In disintegrating the principles into their component facts the principles have been lost sight of. These specialists find it increasingly difficult to discuss let alone agree on the same principles because of differences in the same language. Unified principles can be a means to unite the different branches of knowledge, first by principles, later by common terminology.

Unless the integration and unity of knowledge is achieved the impotence of knowledge and the disintegration of our civilization is anticipated, if not already apparent. Only a universal and eternal method of thought, and universal and eternal standards and values in education, can prevent social disintegration and reaffirm social unity.

The author has written a work which attempts to unify all previous unifying philosophies, or to unify all principles into "unified principles." He does not consider these to be the ultimate knowledge, but does feel a door has been opened and the vast riches within are left to be discovered by others.

In his original work the author applies semantic methods and a system of key words to make practical the application of the power behind unified principles. Such a work is usually read only by the scholar. The author, for greater appeal, has written these stories as a means to express unified principles in more interesting terms.

Each of these stories expresses one or more unified principles. It is a unified principle as evidenced by the fact that any one of these stories can be a basis for explaining thousands of life experiences. They can explain experiences in the past, present, or future, or anywhere in the universe, simply by changing the story's relative values of time, place, individual, circumstance and degree.

The author expects many to have opinions and conclusions that oppose those in these stories. But if the reader will patiently tolerate these differences of opinion he will eventually grasp insight into the principles which are the basic truths to be derived from the stories. The story, its facts, and its conclusions are only the tools by which to achieve insight into unified principles.

The same applies to the concluding proverbs after each story. They are but tools to grasp insight into unified principles. Like all proverbs they have an element of truth in them, but their contradiction indicates a greater truth.

No formal instruction is given in this book to teach unified principles, but the reader will grasp these by insight as he goes along. He will perceive all the different knowledge and wisdom expressed in these stories evolve into a few unified principles. Most of the world's knowledge and wisdom are based on only a few unified principles which can be symbolized by key words: cycle, balance, trinity (positive-neutral-negative), standard, goal, progressive, perspective, relative, moderation, and a few more less significant. When grasped, the significance of these key words may cause an amazing revelation to profoundly effect the reader.

The significance of these key words can be perceived in the subtitles of this work. All stories have their basic principles expressed by only about twenty-five key words. These compose the subtitles. In other words, twenty-five key words can express just about the whole realm of knowledge. Combinations of these key words can consciously and unconsciously "generate" ideas.

Some benefits to be derived from acquiring these unified principles can be as follows:

A means to grasp the spiritual and intellectual wisdom which are missing elements in our materialistic, sensory age of science.

A means to the source of knowledge which enables the supply of proven answers to simplify the most complex and abstract problems.

A means to the roots of the tree of knowledge to which all new knowledge can be readily associated to increase the ability to learn, reason, recall, and create ideas.

A means to better evaluating standards, values, doctrines, and virtues which is a necessity in this age of advertising and propaganda.

A means to a more simple understanding of the psychological, social, and moral nature of the individual, family, group, city, nation, and civilization.

A means to finding common principles in opposing fields of theology, philosophy, and science, or between any spiritual, intellectual, and material knowledge.

A means to perceive, evaluate, understand, predict, and control the various factors that control man and nature.

Besides these general benefits to be derived once, unified principles are grasped, many specific benefits will become apparent to the reader.

The knowledge of unified principles is cumulative and incapable of being forgotten. Once learned, the benefits of unified principles will continue to develop as long as the person has the senses to perceive knowledge.

A TREASURY OF PARABLES

THE DISAGREEABLE FRIENDS

(On relative standards and values)

Two friendly and agreeable men, who rarely ever had a difference of opinion, were so much alike in their size, strength, and tastes that they even looked alike. Even their names, Mike and Ike, were alike.

"Let's go on a hunting trip into the wilderness," said Mike. And of course Ike agreed.

The next day Mike walked the five miles from his home to Ike's home. From there they both walked two miles into the forest. At this point Ike stopped, wiped his brow, and said, "Whew! We certainly have had a long and difficult hike."

"Oh, I don't know," said Mike, "it seemed rather short and easy to me."

This unexpected disagreement struck Ike like unholy profanity. Why had Mike disagreed when obviously the hike was at least a long two miles. He felt concerned but decided not to add fuel to the disagreement so he swallowed his retort.

Arriving at a camp site they both went about gathering rocks for a fireplace. Ike, who had hiked with only his lunch and his gun, picked up a twenty pound boulder and exclaimed, "Whew! Is this rock heavy!"

Mike, who had hiked with forty pounds on his back and twenty pounds in each hand, looked at Ike and jokingly said, "You must be getting weak from overwork, Ike; I'm carrying a boulder twice the size of yours but it doesn't feel heavy at all."

Ike did not take this jokingly for he resented the disagreement by Mike, especially when it was so obvious that his rock was heavy and Mike's rock must have been twice as heavy. Again Ike restrained the impulse to disagree with Mike's disagreement. Their friendship was too great; still, what kind of friend would disagree with an obvious truth?

When the fireplace was finished Ike made coffee for both of them. Ike, who was eating a salty biscuit with his coffee, smacked his lips and said, "Well, I can at least say that I make a fine cup of sweet coffee."

Mike who ate a chocolate bar with his coffee disagreed, "What's wrong with this coffee, Ike; it tastes flat."

This disagreement exasperated Ike to the point where his cumulated resentment was ready to explode in violent argument. But for the greater cause of his friendship he inhibited his opinions of Mike, as the blood within him boiled even more.

As they sat around after lunch Ike complained, "I have so much trouble with my wet feet and with these annoying mosquitoes."

Mike who had twisted his ankle and painfully sprained it was worried about walking back to civilization. His greater pain and troubles made him unconscious of the pain from such insignificant annoyances and troubles as wet feet and mosquitoes. So Mike told Ike, "Maybe these mosquitoes don't like my smell, but I don't feel any bugs biting me, and I don't know why a little thing like wet feet is so much concern and trouble to you."

This was the final molecule of cumulated steam that blew up the pot. Ike could stand no more of Mike's contrariness and his continual disagreement with obvious facts. He had to get away from Mike before he hunted him instead of game. So to give a justifiable reason Ike said he felt ill and started to hike his way back. Mike followed him clumsily with his sprained ankle. This irritated Ike more, and Ike's irritation irritated Mike more, which irritated Ike more. So their disagreement cumulated to the degree of violent hatred for each other.

As they entered the town from where they had started the hunting trip they met a wise, old friend of theirs. This friend, seeing by their mad countenances that a life-long friendship was being disintegrated, made efforts to reunite them. Therefore he insisted over their reluctance that they have a cold beer to cool off their hot emotions. Over their beers in a quiet corner of a tavern the wise friend explained to the friends like a father trying to settle a difference between his sons.

"Now look here, Ike, you resent Mike because he disagreed with you on obvious facts and truths; well, as a friend, would you want Mike to tell you a lie just to agree with you? What kind of a friend would you be? Well, he would have told you a lie if he agreed, for in disagreeing he spoke just as much truth as you, Ike."

"What are you talking about," defended Ike, "how could he be telling the truth in saying that a rock was light when it was twice the size of the heavy rock I carried."

"The truth," said the wise old friend, "is that a ten pound rock seems light after carrying twenty pound rocks, and seems heavy after lifting two pound rocks. A two mile hike is relatively short after hiking ten miles, but long if one has hiked no miles. Sweet coffee after eating sweeter candy is relatively bitter, and sweeter after eating salty biscuits. Pain and trouble seem minor relative to major pain and trouble, and seem major relative to one with no pain or trouble."

At this point loud screaming and roaring, threats and profanity, from a couple who were obviously unhappily married, distracted their attention. But just as suddenly as it started this violent storm subsided and the couple walked away silently, not happily, but at least agreeably.

The two friends turned to each other and held out their hands in friendly reconciliation. Neither said anything but both understood. Relative to the violent disagreement of the married couple their disagreement was insignificant. And relative to the settlement of the married couple their lack of settlement was ridiculous.

Now that they had settled their disagreement and were once more happy in disposition the whole world of nature seemed brighter—and so it was relative to what their happier disposition prepared them to perceive.
Thus:

Troubles seem minor relative to major troubles, and major relative to minor troubles.

Sour makes sweet relatively sweeter; sweet makes sour relatively more sour.

The same line is long or short relative to another line.

THE LOVERS LOST BY LOVE

(On relative standards of love)

A most moral and modest man loved his wife as no man can. No one could love him as much as his wife, and no one was more beautiful and satisfying. He was known to love his wife to such a degree that never had he been out with another woman. Besides, his strict moral character would not permit other women even if he gave himself the opportunity.

Next to his wife this man loved his three children, a daughter and two sons. He did everything possible to make his children happy and to earn their love. No matter what his children did he could always excuse and forgive them to manifest his love and to avoid losing their love. He was so generous and forgiving in his love of his children that his children took him for granted. They could see no reason for expressing their love for him in order to get something or to obtain his forgiveness. They did not love him, still he loved them to such a degree that he forgave their lack of love and offered more generous gifts to obtain their love.

One day this loving man became involved in an argument with his wife over an insignificant trifle. This was a spark that exploded a mass of insignificant trifles that had been repressed and kept smouldering. The quarrel cumulated in rage until he slammed out of the house and headed for the nearest tavern. And as fate would have it he ended up in the arms of a barmaid. This was the first time he had ever been with any woman other than his wife, but it was an affair that changed the whole course of his life.

A few days later, after the fires of his emotion had burned out, he returned to his weeping and forgiving wife. But from that moment on everything about his wife was wrong and worse. Whenever he saw his wife's face he saw the prettier barmaid's face beside it. And as time dragged on slowly, as it will when one is bored, the image of the barmaid's face became more beautiful and in comparison the face of his wife became more ugly. Nothing his wife did could compare with what the barmaid did, and the more he made these comparisons the better the barmaid appeared and the worse his wife was. The more he treated his wife as ugly and unsatisfying the worse she treated him. So the hate for each other cumulated. No one could hate each other as they did.

But this tale of love was not the only failure of love. The eldest son had been permitted by his loving father to be free and carefree in all he did. Never was he disturbed by a mean parent reprimanding or whipping him in cruel punishment. Naturally his freedom exposed him to many experiences with others, especially in the natural pleasures that some foolishly inhibit. When this experienced youth finally married, because of necessity, he really loved his wife as being different from the rest. But when the honeymoon was over he had time to really compare his wife with others he had known. In comparison she was a dull bore. To recapture his past life of love and adventure he began finding excuses to leave his wife at home and to frequent his old haunts and old acquaintances—especially the pretty ones. Within a few short years he deserted his loving wife and disappeared to parts unknown with a female unknown.

The very chaste daughter in this loving family married a very virtuous and innocent young man. Neither had experienced the forbidden pleasures before marriage or with others after marriage. Maybe that is why two years after their wedding day they still loved each other as tenderly and sincerely as on their wedding day. They could expect to love each other for eternity for both saw each other as the ideal love mate. But time came when the husband's absence at work made the loving wife miss him severely. To ease her aching heart she took to watching stories on TV and listening to them on the radio. She preferred romantic love stories because they recalled many of her own beautiful moments of love. But then strange things began to happen. The more she saw and heard radio and TV lovers, the more romantic and gallant they appeared and the more vulgar and crude seemed her husband in comparison. She soon began to find fault with her husband's lack of love because it was so much less romantic than her latest TV idol's way of loving. Soon she was nagging her poor husband to show her disgust for his unromantic crudity. All the while the poor husband never suspected that a TV idol was stealing his wife's love away. When they reached the point of not talking to each other, he took to drinking and she took to sleeping alone to be away from him. Thus it was that the wife's love had destroyed not only her own love but also her husband's.

The last member of this family had a destiny which followed the primrose rather than the thorny path of love. He was an idealistic and aesthetic sort of youth who spent most of his time dreaming and reading beautiful poetry, idealistic fantasies, and romantic epics. His love of women was soft and tender, delicate and aesthetic. But the only women to whom he expressed his love and devotion were in the romantic dream-world of his mind—in the land of chivalrous knights, princesses in distress, and castles in the air. In comparison to these untouchable, chaste, pure, and modest angels, all other women were crude and vulgar peasants. Never could he meet a girl on earth without finding faults to cause his rejection. Someday, he thought, he would in some heroic and romantic event meet the girl of his dreams, his girl without faults, his girl that he could still find in his poetry and literature. At the age of thirty-five he still had not found her. At the age of forty his dreams were shattered and dispersed by reality. He now realized that it was no longer a question of finding his dream girl, but of getting any girl to desire him.

Thus it was that beautiful love was lost to all the members of this family. They lost love because they thought they found a greater love, or because their beautiful dream love made real love seem ugly.

Thus:

A man may have the worst but loves it as the best if he knows of no other.

A man may have the best but loves it least if he dreams of a better.

See love in the actor's eye and you will soon see blemishes on your mate's face.

THE POPULARITY SEEKER

(On balanced moderation)

A shy young lad had difficulty in expressing himself, in getting along with others, and in making friends. In other words, he was unpopular. He was not afraid to admit his problem, face it, and attack it directly. He bought several of the most popular books on "How to Be Popular" and began an intensive self-study course in popularity.

After staying awake nights studying these books and memorizing their basic rules and principles he went out into the world to put his theoretical knowledge into practice.

He learned that positive personalities always have a cheerful smile. So he beamed with a smile even when he felt miserable. Those who tolerated him before now looked at him with suspicion and thought, "What clever scheme lies behind that sinister smirk?" In self-defense they removed their own smiles and scowled back at him.

He learned that he should show interest in others by listening and letting them talk. So he did until he experienced the awkward silence resulting when he met those who could not converse or who had read the same popularity books as he. Those who could converse were exasperated by his lack of conversation and thought him to be an ignorant and unintelligent bore to be avoided.

He learned to be considerate and to never interrupt a speaker. So he never did speak to make himself known.

He learned to be humble and to avoid boasting about his abilities and accomplishments. As a result everyone took him to be a meek and mild fool who never did and never would accomplish anything. How could he when he expressed no abilities that could help others or himself.

He learned to be agreeable and to avoid all antagonizing arguments. He never did get into an argument, but neither did he get any ideas across or prevent others from taking many liberties and advantages of him, because to maintain their friendship he would not disagree with them.

He learned to be positive, to praise on all occasions, and to avoid criticism at all cost. This made others feel so superior they would not associate with one as inferior as he.

He learned not to be negative, to avoid all complaining, and to make no display of past or present misery. So it is understandable why he never received understanding sympathy and was not tolerated for his grouchy disposition when he had a toothache.

He learned to be self-confident, but became so self-conscious of being self-confident and of following the rules of popularity that he lost what little self-confidence he had.

Apparently the rules to achieve popularity were making him lose popularity. So he went to the other extreme. He never smiled and no one ever smiled at him. He monopolized conversation causing others to walk away because they could not talk. His boasting irritated others to desperation. He criticized others to the point of rage. His constant complaining bored to distraction. He interrupted and disagreed with others to start arguments that came near to blows. He went contrary to the rules of popularity and became a crude and vulgar nuisance. He did this until he realized that he not only had no friends but had acquired many enemies.

In disgust he said, "To heck with personality! I'll get along without trying to." And to his surprise he observed that in losing his consciousness of being for or against the rules of popularity he had lost his self-consciousness and became more conscious of others. This made him more interested in their interests, which improved his self-confidence and made him more ready to praise others. This made others think he had certain abilities which he did not have, so he had no need to boast. This gave him a pleasant smile and a pleasing disposition that eliminated his reasons for complaining.

He had finally matured. He was no longer an adolescent seeking to find the personality that best suited himself. He had found himself. He had learned to express his own natural character.

Thus:

Moderation between the extremes is better.

When morons try to act like geniuses they become idiots.

We are born to play a role, not another role.

THE GOOD BOY AND THE BAD BOY

(On relative standards of the good-bad balance)

Two brothers were having a bitter, unbrotherly dispute when their mother intervened. To let her sons release any unspent emotion from their systems she let each freely express his rage to her.

The son whom she considered to be the good boy of the family said resentfully, "Why do I, who have received nothing but the highest praise and award for good behavior, now receive nothing but reprimand and criticism? Yet all I do is still of the highest standard. Maybe I should act in an opposite manner? Maybe I should act like a bad boy, not a good boy, in order to be commended?"

The son whom the mother considered to be the bad boy of the family said in a puzzled manner, "That is why my brother started this argument with me. Even so, I will be honest enough to say that he probably has good reason for his resentment. For why do I, who have been unworthy of praise and award for good behavior, receive nothing but praise and approval when all I do is of much lower standard than my good brother. Maybe I should not try to improve my behavior if it means I will get the poor consideration my good brother is getting?"

The wise mother had never realized that this bitter feeling had existed between her sons because of her apparent unfair treatment of them. But now that she realized it the answer became clear. Turning to her unhappy good son she said sympathetically, "I am sincerely sorry, my son, but the reason you are always being criticized, even tho you strive to act the best you can, is that you have reached the top of the ladder of goodness and success. You have no room left to advance or to improve in, and praise is given only to those who advance or improve. You can hardly move without falling backward, and criticism goes to those who fall back."

Turning to her bad son the wise mother said, "And you, my son, are at the bottom of the ladder of goodness and success. You can hardly move without making some praise-worthy advance, and you have little room left to fall back to. So even tho you are much worse in behavior than your good brother, you still receive more praise for doing better and for not doing worse than you normally do."

From that day on this wise mother never failed to praise her good son's high standard of behavior before criticizing any backward slip he happened to make. Thus the emotional effect of her negative criticism was neutralized by her positive praise.

In addition she made it a rule never to criticize her good son or her bad son, even tho the quality of their behavior was vastly different, so long as they followed her constant advice to "Do the best you can." As no one can do better than the best, so no one deserves criticism for doing the best he can even tho it be bad by other standards. Thus:

When we reach the top we either stay or fall; when we reach the bottom we either stay or climb.

The light is unnoticed until it becomes dimmer or brighter; the good is unnoticed until it becomes better or worse.

We cannot have good without a bad to compare it with; we cannot have bad without a good to compare it with.

THE GOOD WORKER AND THE POOR WORKER

(On relative standards of the positive-negative balance)

A conscientious, industrious, and productive worker felt he had a grievance. Another worker who was generally known to be careless, carefree, and lazy had been promoted over him. In fact, neither the good nor the poor worker could understand why the promotion had been made under these obviously unfair conditions. Neither knew the answer, nor could they get it in their shop, so both contacted the business agent of their union who was reputed to have much wisdom.

The poor worker explained his side of the grievance first. "It seems strange to me," he said, "that I, a poor worker, am promoted over the good worker. I am often tardy and absent. I leave my machine often to talk to other workers. I am a slow, lazy worker who always seeks to avoid extra work. I make many mistakes for which I am often called to the office to correct. My machine is never cared for and is always breaking down. With such traits I am often criticized. I am not one to complain of my promotion; still, I am curious to know why?"

The wise man said nothing until the good worker gave his side of the picture which was stated as follows: "Why should the poor worker be promoted over me? I am never tardy or absent. I never leave my machine to talk to other workers. I work so hard and efficiently that additional work is often given to me, which I do without complaint. My work is so accurate that I have never been corrected for mistakes. I am loyal to the company and have never refused to work overtime. I maintain my machine so that it never breaks down. With such good traits I am never criticized. Why, in the name of Justice, is the poor worker promoted over me when he does the opposite?"

The wise and experienced union business agent smiled a cynical smile as if he had heard this grievance many times in his life. He said sympathetically to the good worker, "It is a strange paradox of this world that most things are not what they seem, and most things that should be are not so. In your perplexing paradox we could say truthfully, even if not apparently, that men are rewarded for what they do; what they do must be seen to be rewarded; what is seen depends upon whose eyes see it. Thus whenever the poor worker was tardy or absent his need was appreciated when someone less trained had to take his place. Whenever he left his machine to converse with others he, without trying to, learned about other machines and how these specific machines all coordinated in the overall production plan. This gave the poor worker a broad perspective of the company's operation, supervision, and administration. He came to know those to whom he talked, and they came to know him. So he acquired many friends who could speak well of him. His slow work and many mistakes caused his supervisors to discuss more efficient methods with him, which also taught him how to instruct other workers. So you can see that the poor worker learned more about the job than you, good worker, who did such a good job that your supervisors could ignore you for you gave them no reasons for concern. Whenever the poor worker's machine broke down he learned about repairing machines. Every criticism taught him something new, and it especially taught him how to accept criticism from his supervisors. So obviously the poor worker knew more about the overall operation, supervision, and administration of the company. He knew more about worker relations, more about correcting mistakes, and more about repairing machines. Are not these the qualities that make a good supervisor? As a good worker you knew only your own particular job which was but a cog in the whole operation. You knew nothing of the overall plan of operation. You knew no other workers nor how to get along with fellow workers. You knew nothing of other machines nor how to repair them. Could such a person be a supervisor?"

The good worker's tense resentment had relaxed with understanding, but now he appeared limp and numb with hopeless futility at having worked so conscientiously for nothing. But he regained enough fortitude, spirit, and composure to say, "I must agree with what you say, but why should I continue to be a good worker? Why should I not act like the poor worker and be rewarded for doing nothing?"

The old union man, with a far-away look in his eyes as if reviewing his past struggles, said after a moment, "What I have said is true, but if this were all to truth then truth deserves to be suppressed if it serves to encourage the bad and discourages the good. But have faith in the fact that good is rewarded and retribution comes to those who deserve it. The deceiving, undeserving, poor worker may succeed and hold positions long enough to get promotions, but time tests the quality of all things. The poor worker who succeeds temporarily must keep changing his position as his true nature is revealed, or he is expelled when his good personality is not worth his poor production. On the other hand, the good worker's true nature is perceived in time if he has the patience to endure that long. Be patient, good worker, time will reward you, but meanwhile, maybe I can speed this time by acting on your grievance with the powers that be."

Both the good worker and the poor worker thanked the wise business agent for his advice and both left wiser than when they came. From that day on the good worker acted

more like the poor worker to gain more supervisory qualities, and the poor worker acted more like the good worker to
make his position more permanent.

Thus:

Reward to make action; punish to repress action; do
neither to confuse action.

Evil may be rewarded and good punished in the present,
but the future brings just retribution.

Truth should be suppressed when it encourages evil and
discourages good.

THE STERN AND THE POPULAR PRINCIPALS

(On the cyclical changes of perspective)

The citizens of a town were enraged because their children were lawless and not learning a thing at school. Some of them said angrily, "We need a stern disciplinarian to control and teach the lawless children." So a stern, unsmiling disciplinarian was made principal.

In carrying out his responsibilities the principal had students spanked, placed in dunce corners, and detained after school. He failed some and made them repeat the year. He suspended some until their unconcerned parents came in for consultation. He expelled others to live with parents who were too busy to bother with them. Soon there was much agitation as students complained to parents, and parents complained to politicians, and politicians complained to the superintendent. The competent superintendent promptly discharged the stern principal for incompetent abuse and maltreatment of students. This charge and discharge so blackened his professional reputation that never again could he teach or administer in any other school. So he went to work in a factory on an assembly line. There he was much happier doing less work for more money and with no students or parents to make him miserable.

The citizens of the town then hired a principal who was well-known for his pleasant smile and popular personality. He came to a school that was well-disciplined by the exhausting efforts of the former stern principal. His discipline had made them self-disciplined. The popular principal came to a school where well-behaved children were eager to learn and where students had learned to respect teachers and even the stern principal just before he was discharged. The popular principal came just in time to get all the credit for all the good work done by the stern disciplinarian.

One parent said, "We had so much trouble before, so many complaints; now we have none. Our new principal should be commended." Another said, "The former principal was unfriendly and stern; I did not like him. The new principal is so friendly and so relaxed; I like him." Children liked him because he did not punish them; he let them do as they pleased, for as he so often said, "I love these children too much to hurt them by punishment." Parents liked him for he never complained about their children and always went out of his way to tell all of them what fine children they had. He placed no children in dunce corners, for as he told parents, "They are all bright children." And of course no one ever failed in his school or repeated a school year. One parent said, "My child always failed and was always being punished by the disciplinarian; now he never fails and is never punished. Our very popular principal must be doing a very fine job of teaching our children." Another said, "We never hear bad things about the school; all we hear are good things; he must be a wonderful principal."

Praise travels fast and the popular principal was invited to take over the administration of a larger school at double his salary. He was to replace a stern disciplinarian who had been asked to resign because of his abuse of authority and mistreatment of students. The popular principal accepted this position just as the citizens from his former school began to realize that vice, vandalism, and viciousness were again rampant at their school.

Again they angrily complained, "We need a stern disciplinarian to control and teach these lawless children." They got a stern principal, but they discharged him as being too severe as soon as he had restored law, order, and learning in the school. Again the stern principal's reputation was blacklisted and never again could he administer or teach in a school. Again they hired a popular principal who again claimed all the credit for all the good work of the stern principal. Eventually when all stern principals were driven from all schools, the popular principals controlled all education. When parents angrily complained of lawlessness and lack of learning, they were appeased with a pleasant smile of understanding. These smiles became sickening to the parents when they finally realized that there were no stern principals left to restore law, order, and learning in their school. Then it was that dark ignorance and illiteracy, frightful anarchy and chaos, and gloomy depression and dejection descended upon this once brilliant, educated, civilized town and nation.

Thus:

Builders of the future are criticized in the present; builders of the present are criticized in the future.

The disciplined criticize in the present but praise in the future.

Credit today's good or evil on past, not present leaders.

THE JUDOIST

(On judo resistance and the balance of control)

In days of old when knights were bold, outlaws did harm but monks would not arm. One day a knight and a monk traveled a deserted road near their castle and monastery. The mighty knight, having left his armor at the castle, said to the monk, "My size and strength make me fear no man. I am hard enough to withstand any beating. Let those who would attack beware."

The meek monk, from the Judoist Order which practiced submission to a higher Will, answered softly, "Your size and strength are as impressive as your boasts. I am small and weak, and must depend upon my spirit and my mind to survive, not my body. But sometimes the meek inherit the earth, not the strong."

The robust knight laughed and retorted, "You are a weak fool to believe the mind and spirit are stronger than the body in physical combat."

Instead of denying or resisting this charge the Judoist bent under the attack and agreed, "Yes," he said, "I suppose I am a fool to believe the weak can conquer the strong."

If he denied being a fool he would, in effect, affirm the knight was wrong. The frustrated knight would then emotionally argue to prove himself right. Emotion would close his ears to reason. But he could not argue with what he agreed. The monk's lack of resistance elated the knight and prepared him to listen. The Judoist then counterattacked, "Yes, I am a weak fool," he said, "but sometimes frail, bending reeds survive storms that shatter mighty, unbending oaks."

At this moment four bandits surrounded them with obvious manifestations of using clubs on them. Unarmed, the travelers were in a dilemma. They could valiantly defend themselves to death and lose all, or passively surrender and hope to escape with their lives.

The physically strong but mentally weak knight met the challenge and prepared for battle.

The physically weak but mentally strong monk had a negative first reaction of fear. Instead of impulsively reacting to this overwhelming fear he self-disciplined himself to do something consciously. He controlled his spirit, mind, and body, and his emotional impulse to run by standing dead-still. He thus regained conscious control of his actions over his uncontrollable subconscious emotions. His controlled reason was then better prepared to perceive and evaluate the situation. His controlled body was then better prepared to act under his controlled mind.

The Judoist, realizing it was better to bend than to be broken, acquiesced passively. "I will not resist," he said to the bandits, "here is my money."

The brave knight resisted aggressively. "You cowardly dog!" he said to the monk, "I will fight them alone."

The attackers, overconfident at the Judoist's manifest lack of resistance, ignored him to concentrate their attack on the belligerent knight. The knight warded off their blows head-on with hands and arms—which were shattered. He charged in head first to butt his attackers and his skull was fractured. Without arms to cushion his fall or to control his rolling he hit the ground with a thud that broke two ribs. His resistance continued as he kicked with his feet. The greater his resistance the more vicious his punishment and the more terrible his destruction. In resisting hopeless odds

he suffered the consequences. He was destroyed physically—
he was dead.

Their violent emotions released, the bandits relaxed their
weapons and turned to the Judoist. While he remained dead-
still he created no action to cause violent reactions from the
bandits. In bending to their will and agreeing with manifest humility and servility to part with his money, no force
was necessary.

As the bandits were leaving with their loot one of them
decided there should be no witness to the crime. After all,
the death penalty would be no worse for another murder.
He swung his club at the Judoist, but did no damage for it
was met by an unresisting hand which fell back as in catch-
ing a fast ball. The Judoist calmly bent his body to avoid
another blow and then counterattacked to push the attacker's arm in the direction of its motion. The attacker's arm,
meeting no resisting reaction, threw him off balance and out
of control. It was like suddenly pulling open a door just as
someone pushes hard against the other side. The bandit
flew thru the air, upsetting another bandit on the way.

The other two bandits attacked simultaneously and
would have overwhelmed the Judoist had he not consciously
and unresistingly fallen. Their heavy clubs clumsily fanned
the air. As their momentum met no resistance their clubs
flew out of control and pushed in their surprised faces.
The relaxed Judoist remained limp and made no effort to
brace himself. Like a somersaulting tumbler he rolled when
he hit the ground and was not even bruised.

Before the bandits could recover their senses, balance,
and control, the Judoist retreated to the protective conceal-
ment of the forest. Here he prepared plans for retreating to
reserve forces in the rear in order to cumulate power to
equalize, or overbalance that of the bandits. The more he
retreated the more he controlled the situation.

As the bandits searched for him they went further from
their known home grounds, while losing attacking momen-

tum, unified power, and control of the situation. Already they dissipated their united power in separating to find him. As time increased their emotional frustration, in balance, it decreased their sober reasoning.

Because the bandits were divided, the Judoist could attack each individually with an equal balance of power. He had the added advantage of knowing his enemies' strength and weapons. A man with a weapon may master a giant, but a midget with a better weapon can master both. He decided against attacking the bandits, for violence was contrary to his creed; besides, they too could apply the Judo Principle by falling back to unite their strength for a counterattack. But in reserve for any eventuality he carried a club that was bigger and better than any carried by the bandits.

He retreated to where he had previously passed the camp of three travelers. He joined them to equalize the balance of power against the bandits. To avoid personal violence he persuaded the three to retreat to the castle where the bandits would dare not approach.

At the castle the knights were aroused over their comrade's slaying. They quickly organized to counterattack the unsuspecting bandits who were distracted in tracking the monk.

When the bandits saw the knights their self-controlled attacking action turned to a defensive reaction controlled by the counterattack. Their confident spirit of victory became a stifling fear of defeat. Their panic created an uncontrolled rout, not a controlled judoist retreat. This prevented any controlled counterattack on their part. Their blind emotional panic caused them to be ambushed and slain without loss to the knights.

That night, in the great banquet hall of the castle, the knights celebrated their victory. The walls rang with toasts to the physical valor and gory glory of their triumphant battle. Wine-swollen tongues jeered the frail, fearful monk who had cowardly run from battle and who had crawled to them—brave, strong knights—to have them fight for might and right.

If they could hear thru beer-blurred ears, their whiskey-whipped brains would not have comprehended the Judoist's stock answer as he unresistingly ignored their jeers: "Frail, bending reeds survive storms that shatter mighty, unbending oaks."

Thus:

The obedient dog gets meat; the growling dog gets beat.

The strong destroy the weak who resist them and keep the weak who assist them.

Judo is the controlled bending before superior force, causing it to lose control, in order to prepare reserves to counterattack and control.

THE FIVE DECISIONS

(On the positive-neutral-negative achievement of goals)

Five travelers halted at a road junction. Before they could move on they had to decide which road in the junction to take. They finally decided on one road and rejected the other and were again on their way. In order to reach their major goal, a large city, they had to reach many minor goals, the smaller cities on the way. They did not have too much difficulty until their goal was blocked by a river whose bridge was destroyed. Beyond that a muddy avalanche blocked the road. The broken bridge stopped them, the avalanche would only have slowed them. The five travelers stopped; they could not move until they had made a decision regarding the barrier and resistance in the path of their goal. Finally, each of them made a decision, but each decision was different.

One traveler said, "I will take this nearby path. I do not know where it leads but it does appear to be a pleasant and easy path that will not require much effort."

The second traveler said, "I will walk downstream; maybe I will find another bridge which will eventually lead me to my original goal."

The third traveler said, "I did not want to go to the city anyway. I am returning to the road junction. There I will take the other road and let it lead me where it will."

The fourth traveler said wearily, "Why go on! We will

never reach the city! It is hopeless! What is the use of even trying any more!" He then sat down, buried his head in his hands, and wept bitterly in self-pity and remorse.

The fifth traveler was made of sterner stuff. He said firmly, "In order to achieve my original goal I will reject those paths that may have less obstacles but whose end is questionable. My original goal has greater value but it will require much greater self-disciplined effort to achieve it. I will swim across the river to avoid going around it. I will climb over the avalanche to avoid going around the mountain. I am determined to achieve my goal as directly as I can."

Whatever course these travelers took their conflict was decided and they could now act to accomplish something— for better or worse. That is, all but the traveler who had given up hope and had sat down. He did nothing, so he accomplished nothing.

The leisurely traveler who had evasively taken the easy path was happy until he realized that the path led nowhere. He wandered in aimless confusion by going around in blind circles.

The traveler who had evasively walked around the river and the mountain to indirectly achieve his goal finally reached the city after many more days of travel than he had planned. But he felt no happier about it for his elation in achieving his goal was neutralized by his frustration in not achieving the minor goals that were on the original road he had resolved to take.

The traveler, who had evasively returned to the road junction to take the other road in order to reach his goal, finally settled in a strange town when he ran out of funds. He was no happier in this town for he was forever disturbed as he dreamed of the happier times he might have had had he gone on to the other city.

The traveler with the self-disciplined character, who had attacked and overcome all the barriers and resistances in his path, had directly achieved his goal and reached the city with beaming elation. He was elated by crossing the river, more elated by climbing over the avalanche, and tremendously elated by reaching the city.

The frustrated traveler who had lost all hope and all will to go on had no further goals to achieve. He just sat there and sadly brooded like a suffering martyr until he died of starvation—for without goals he could not move from the spot.

Thus:

How we overcome conflicts, barriers, resistance, and frustrations to achieve goals determines character and personality.

Achievement elates; frustration deflates; conflict confuses.

One degree of achievement plus two degrees of frustration neutralize to one degree of frustration.

THE SNOW-COVERED FIELD

(On the positive-neutral-negative achievement of goals)

A blizzard the night before had piled up drifts of snow over the land. Next morning an experienced old grandfather asked his young grandson to go to the store on the other side of an open field. The grandson took one look at the deep snow and protested, "But, Grandpa, I don't want to go; that snow is too deep for me."

The wise old grandfather took the boy to a window overlooking the snow-covered field and pointing to it he said, "Did you know that how you achieve your goals will determine your character? Your character is like that snow-covered field. If your goal is to reach the other side of the field, you may indirectly achieve your goal by evasively walking around all the snow drifts. But you will leave a long, crooked path in the snow. Or you may indirectly achieve your goal by going for a more easily achieved goal, such as taking that plowed road to another store which is three times as far away. In this way you will leave no path on the field. Or you may directly achieve your goal by pushing thru the snow drifts to leave a straight path. Or you may give up all hope of achieving your goal, as you do now, by staying in your nice, warm home."

The boy perked up, rubbed his hands together, and said, "That is what I want to do—stay home by this nice, warm fireplace."

"Never mind," said the grandfather reproachfully, "what you decide now will be the decision or path you take the next time. The more your path is taken the more the snow is beaten down to make it easier to take the next time. Soon the straight path thru the snow that required greater effort at first becomes a quick and easy means to achieving your future goal of crossing the field. The crooked path around the snowdrifts that required less effort at first becomes a slow, difficult means to achieving the same goal from that time on."

"But that requires so much effort," whined the warm and comfortable lad.

"Maybe so," said the grandfather, "but if you stay at home, you will find it more difficult to leave on the second day, and more difficult the third, until you realize you have become a hermit who is afraid to leave the shelter of his home. Once you have beaten a crooked path thru the snow you can change it to a straight one only by the strongest self-disciplined effort."

"You're convincing me, Grandpa," said the boy. "I'm beginning to feel like a hermit already."

"I am glad to hear you can understand this," answered the grandfather, "but let me explain how this can make you happier. The attacking of your goal by making a straight path has positive value and will give you positive emotions. Retreating from your goal by staying home has negative value and will give you negative emotions. Indirectly achieving your goal by evading the obstacles before it has neutral value and will cause no change in your emotions. This is because the positive emotions of your goal achievement are neutralized by the negative emotions of not overcoming the obstacles before this goal. These obstacles are actually minor goals. So to acquire will power and happiness, directly attack your goals."

"Say no more, Grandpa," said the grandson. "Where is

my hat and coat? I am going to beat the straightest path across that field you ever saw."

Thus:

The more we achieve the easier it is to achieve; the more we fail to achieve the easier it is to fail.

How we achieve the first time determines how we achieve the second time and into the future.

The strong attack; the weak evade; the lost retreat.

THE RADICAL'S LAMENT

(On deranging progressive ranges of perspective and goals)

A young college student who was well-educated, but not very learned or wise, reached the idealistic stage of renouncing his family as ignorant, his patriotism as emotionalism, and his religion as superstition. But soon after he was heard to lament, "Oh, what shall I do! I renounced my religious, patriotic, and family goals. Now I have no goals to achieve. I must have a goal to balance and integrate my spiritual, mental, and physical activity and to give me a reason for being. Without a goal I have nothing to work, fight, or die for. I must find a goal that is higher and broader than my personal goals. In order to achieve this I will join a radical group and fight for its idealistic goals. Good or bad, this group and its cause will give me goals to strive for. This group will give me a feeling of belonging and a reason for being."

So the idealistic youth joined a radical group to work, fight, and if need, die for its cause. But it was not long before his realistic experiences with neurotic cliques and power-mad leaders made him skeptical of his ideals and cynical of his education. He was fighting to save the world but he did not have a friend in the world. In fighting to save the world he never had time to consider his personal needs and benefits. In the dark solitude of his dingy cellar-room he lamented to himself, "In accepting the idealistic, broad range future goals of radicalism I have lost sight of realistic, narrow range present goals for myself, my family, and my nation. In upgrading radicalism I have degraded myself. In rejecting achievable goals that bring happiness, I have accepted unachievable goals that only bring frustrated unhappiness. In disillusionment I must reject these radical goals to accept more achievable goals. I will return to religious, patriotic, and family goals."

The disillusioned and cynical youth eased out of the radical group and shame-faced returned to his home, his nation, and his religion. But the welcome he received was frigid and unforgiving. Now his lamenting became a wailing as he talked to himself, for he had no one else to whom he could talk the poison out of his system.

"Woe is me," he wailed, "radicalism has degraded my personality and reputation. Everyone now ostracizes me. No longer can I say, 'My family, my country, my religion.' What an empty, dead feeling this gives me. Even radicals denounce and hate me for having left them. As a social outcast I can no longer strive for the goals of my family, country, or religion, even if I wanted to. I have no goals to give me a reason for being or to integrate my spiritual, mental, and physical activity. I have nothing to live for. Maybe alcohol, narcotics, or suicide will solve the problem. Maybe it is just as easy to pass into the insane world of happy delusions. Woe is me! I must stop this mental derangement and disintegration. I must return to radicalism even tho I become an unthinking robot whose will is enslaved to unachievable goals. At least I will have a reason for spiritual, mental, and physical activity. Oh, why did I renounce the virtues, honor, and duties of my religious, patriotic, and family goals!"

Thus:

Without goals to integrate spiritual, mental, and physical activity, man has no reason for activity—no reason for being.

Frustrated and unhappy are idealists for their goals can never be achieved.

Who would reform the world deforms himself; who reforms himself reforms the world.

THE FIGHTER

(On deranging the progressive ranges of society and goals)

An idealistic young man once went off to fight a war, for as he thought, "I joined this army to fight the noble cause and ideals of world peace."

But becoming disillusioned by the unidealistic realities of war, he thought, "World peace is a crazy idea. Now I fight only as a patriot to defend my country."

But his patriotism and service to his country were ignored to the degree where he began to think, "What an ungrateful country! I now fight only for the glory of my army regiment."

But the commander of the regiment failed to recognize his services either and he began to think, "Who cares for regimental glory! I now fight only for the pride of my army company."

But when not too many in his company showed him friendship, he thought, "To heck with army pride! I will fight only to be loyal to the friends in my army squad."

But after a member of his squad betrayed his trust he thought, "You can't trust anyone! Who wants to be friends! I can do without them. I am now fighting only for myself. To heck with everybody else!"

Not long after, as a sad, lonely and miserable drunkard in a dirty and dingy tavern, he thought, "Oh miserable me! What can I fight for? Without goals I have no hope; without hope I have no reason for being; without a reason for being, why be? So, I must either end my being quickly by suicide, slowly by alcohol, or live in the happy world of insane dreams."

Just then the bartender came over and said, "Hey, Buddy, there's a party going on next door. You look like you could make use of it. Why don't you give it a try?"

The unhappy man, who had no reason for being, automatically refused. But with a little more sympathy from the bartender he realized that some people, even if only a strange bartender, were willing to give him recognition. A little more sympathy, a little more persuasion, and a little more beer on the house added more encouragement. By deciding to go to the party he had some kind of reason for being which gave him enough spirit and will power to get off his bar stool and head for the party. At the party he met a sympathetic girl who suggested further meetings. This gave him greater reasons for being and for living. Then they were married and bought a cottage for themselves. This gave him still more reasons for being. When children arrived, he realized he now had something to be proud of, something to work for, to fight for, and if need be to die for.

From that day on he had goals to achieve which inspired him with hope. Now he had many good reasons for being. Now he wanted to live and to enjoy life by avoiding death, alcohol, and daydreams.

Thus:

No goals, no hope; no hope, no reason for being; no reason for being, no being.

Major causes inspire great hope; minor causes inspire little hope.

Consider the world and you do not consider yourself; consider yourself and you do not consider the world.

THE LADDER OF LIFE

(On deranging the progressive range of freedom and goals)

James Moderf was a cute, helpless, little baby. After bawling for and receiving attention he gurgled to himself in a super-intelligent sort of way, "All I worry about is my own food and comfort. Who wants freedom when they can get such affection and attention as I?"

Jimmy became an active child with revolutionary ideas of independence. "All I care for," he hollered, "is myself; but I suppose if I have to I'll care for my parents too."

When his mother reprimanded him for disobedience he ran away, shouting as he slammed the door behind him, "Now I'm free of my mother's authority! Now I'll find freedom on the outside!"

But outside the security of his family home, Jimmy found that in order to survive and to achieve his goals he had to increase his responsibilities to himself and to the policeman on the beat. These increased social responsibilities caused a balancing decrease in his personal freedom. A good spanking from his father soon ended this exploration into freedom.

Jimmy Moderf the child became Jim the adolescent, and more conscious of his social responsibilities. Contemplating his neighborhood friends he thought, "I'm too self-conscious; I should be more conscious of my parents and of my friends too."

His self-consciousness decreased as he increased his consciousness of a pretty, blonde, blue-eyed classmate. The ethereal cloud of emotional love concealed from him the facts of logical reality. He could not perceive that in gaining freedom to go steadily with this girl of his dreams he had lost his freedom to go with other girls and with boy friends.

As Jim's love for his girlfriend increased it decreased for the members of his boys' club. After an argument with the club's president he said, "Now I'm free of that low-brow leader and his childish codes and customs. Now I will truly find freedom somewhere in this city."

Graduating from high school, Jim felt that he was a man, but wasn't quite sure that he wasn't a youth. In an idealistic mood he told his loved one, "Now we are free of the rules and restrictions imposed by our school; we can also be free of our parents' control. Let's plan our own lives. Let's find true freedom and happiness in the love of married life."

Later, over a beer at the neighborhood tavern, Jim said rather skeptically to his good friend, Lou Lakidar, "Oh, if I had only known how the responsibilities of marriage would frustrate my freedom. If I had only known how the responsibilities of family life and employment would frustrate our freedom to plan our own lives."

Lou Lakidar nodded sympathetically and ordered another beer. He had his own problems on freedom and responsibility to worry about.

At twenty-one, Jim the youth became James Moderf the free man—or so he thought. The thrill of the honeymoon had worn off and his children's screams of pleasure became an irritating nuisance to him. He looked around for other interests and became involved in city political activity. "I'm interested in myself first," he said when asked about his interests and goals, "then my family, my social group, and my city."

But he became disillusioned by frustration in trying to personally change city life. He exiled himself from the raw realities of political life in his city with this cynical explanation, "Now I am free of the political graft and corruption of this city's mayor. Now I will find true freedom somewhere in this nation."

But in evading the responsibilities of one city, Jim acquired them in the next. So his hopes and interests were raised to a higher and broader range. He assumed there would be no corruption in the more dignified higher levels of social and political life and became interested in national cultural and political activities. He expressed his interests and goals in this manner, "I consider myself first, then if I can, I consider my family, group, city, and then my nation."

When he disagreed with what he considered a degrading trend in national progress and could do nothing about it, he emigrated to another nation. His opinion as reported by the press was, "Now that I am free of the oppression and tyranny of that nation's tyrant I will surely find freedom somewhere in this broad civilization of ours."

Old age came, as it does to all men, and experience had molded its expected pattern. Philosophically reminiscing on his past life, Jim Moderf expounded profoundly to any one who would listen to his wisdom, "Listen, lad, and benefit by my experience. Take care of yourself first, then your family, group, city, nation, and civilization—in that order if you can."

But even philosophical Jim could become disgustedly disturbed by the dissipation and degradation of his civilization. At his hardened and brittle age he could not adjust and conform to these changes in progress. So he fled in fearful frustration to a cave in the hills which was unmarred by civilized influences. Now he could consider only himself and his God—in that order. He became an ascetic, religious hermit who occasionally consoled himself by muttering, "Now I have finally found freedom!"

One day he mumbled a complaint, "This religious negativism and asceticism is inhibiting my freedom. I should consider my civilization's welfare more, and maybe even my nation. Maybe I should return to the city to restore my friendships and my family life. Maybe I will find greater freedom by becoming more involved with people."

So Jim Moderf the hermit confiscated some garments off a farmer's clothesline and abandoned his bearskin covering. He deserted his cave to find freedom among the civilized nationalists in the city where his friends, family, and he belonged. . . .

Value judgments being individual and subjective, Jim Moderf grew up and progressively adjusted and conformed to the objective, broadening values of his family, group, city, nation, and civilization—in that order on the progressive ranges of society. All his childhood friends did not develop such maturity as to encompass all these progressively broadening ranges of society. A babyhood friend who became an orphan acquired his own individual values and goals. The feuding families down the street stopped growing at the values of their own families. Members of a self-sufficient gossip circle in the neighborhood stopped maturing at the group level. The partisan politician of Jim's political ward broadened until he reached the range of city politics. Another friend became a national congressman and had his ambitions and interests satisfied at the national range. His quiet, meditating school friend became a philosophy professor. He traveled thru all the progressive ranges of life to be the most fully experienced and the most broad-minded of Jim Moderf's friends.

Lou Lakidar was another childhood friend of Jim Moderf. He was a brilliant boy who developed the same broadening interests and goals as did Jim. At least he did so until he reached the chivalrous, idealistic, and medieval phase of life—adolescence. Then he seemed to lose sight of sensual realism as he gained insight into mental idealism.

From a narrow range interest in his neighborhood boys' club, Lou suddenly became interested only in the broad range goals of world unity, world peace, and universal and eternal brotherly love and cooperation. Of course he bypassed such mundane and trivial goals that had to do with himself, his family, group, city, nation, and civilization.

Excess mental insight made Lou absent-minded of the exterior physical and social realities needed to balance his lop-sided perspective. As a radical idealist he attempted to reach the top of the ladder of life without climbing each step. He was like an unkempt hobo rushing in to demand membership in an exclusive professors' club. He was out of his range and was often kicked back down the steps of progress.

In striving for theoretical ideals, Lou reached for the moon but could not see the ground over which he stumbled and fell. In striving to cure the world before himself, he cured neither himself nor any range below the world level. Never achieving his idealistic goals, Lou developed the morose attitude of bitter frustration. Many considered him odd, if not maladjusted or outright crazy, and ostracized and resisted him accordingly. Those who knew better said he was in a condition of derangement. Lou was more to be pitied than censured were it not for his radical activity which unintentionally disturbed the tranquility of his family, group, city, and nation. The sad paradox of it all was that in fanatically dedicating his life to brotherly love in the world, he did much to destroy it completely as it effected him personally.

Eventually his failure to achieve unachievable, idealistic world goals made Lou quit in frustrated fury. But having no national, city, or group goals as a reserve to fall back on, he had the horrible feeling of not belonging to any group. In helpless loneliness he fell thru the dark void, with a shocking thud, to the bottom of the ladder of life.

In seeking to find his proper place on the ladder of life, Lou went to the other extreme of a worldly attitude to become childish in his attitude toward his family. But his disintegrating family, after years of tolerating his contempt for family unity in favor of world unity, had nothing to do with him.

After years of accepting antagonism and resistance with idealistic brotherly love and tolerance, the balance swung to the other extreme. He became a hater of humanity, an anti-social cynic, an advocate of violent destruction of all he once wanted to improve.

Having nothing greater than himself to work, fight, and die for; having no goals beyond personal goals to integrate his spiritual, mental, and physical activity; and having no broad range goals to give him a reason for being; his unified personality disintegrated.

With only personal goals to hold him together morally, mentally, and physically, Lou became a hermit like Jim Moderf. But where Jim broadened his perspective and goals to become a hermit, Lou narrowed his ranges to become a hermit. Lou's conscious hermitage could not endure too long and he eventually became an unconscious hermit. He degraded and became a deranged derelict on the vast, lonely ocean of life—he became a broken bum.

As Lou decreased his idealism, in balance, he increased his realism. As he narrowed the range of his conscious mind perception, in balance, he broadened the range of his subconscious mind perception. His unselfish idealistic goals allowed no room for selfish personal goals. Having lived in the mental world of idealism so long, the sensual world of reality was a stranger to him. Incapable of adjusting to this stranger, or in achieving its brotherly love, he turned back from the world of sense reality to his own world of mental reality. Lou progressively became more degraded and deranged. As he progressively narrowed the range of his sensual world, in balance, he progressively broadened the mental ranges of fantasy. In the rearrangement of his subconscious mind, after the derangement of his conscious mind, he broadened from delusions to illusions to hallucinations.

Lou Lakidar still had these fantasic dreams as his friend, Jim Moderf, looked at him sitting in the corner of his ward at the state mental hospital. He was still in the strait-jacket placed on him after one of his cyclical periods of maniacal violence. He had just gone thru one of his misanthropic and nihilistic moods in which he wanted to destroy all that he spent his life to improve—world unity, world peace, and universal and eternal brotherly love and cooperation. Now he just stared blankly, but with an ecstatic, radiant sort of happiness as he talked to himself—or we should say to the friends and enemies, angels and devils, that populated his own world of dreams.

He did not hear his friend, Jim Moderf, say to the attendant, "Who is to say which world is more real or better—his or mine."

Thus:

The broader the range of goals, the broader the range of responsibilities, and the less the range of personal freedom.

The socially adjusted cares for himself first, then his family, group, city, nation, and civilization—in that progressive order.

The deranged, striving for broad range goals before narrow range goals are achieved, have no narrow range goals to fall back on when broad range goals are frustrated—and so disintegrate.

Civilizations rise as man considers his own goals, then his family, group, city, nation, and civilization—and declines in reverse order.

THE MEEK MANIAC

(On cumulating the cause-effect balance)

This is a tale of a meek, mild-mannered man who was never known to have been emotionally enraged or profane. It seems that he had a chronic headache bothering him, so he volunteered for psychological treatment of it.

While registering at the hospital he resented the abuse being shown a mental patient. On politely and gently expressing his resentment to an attendant he was contemptuously ordered to, "Sit down and mind your own business!" This rudeness upset his calm composure and intensified his painful headache. He had voluntarily entered the hospital so he decided to voluntarily leave it. But in registering as a patient he had become an inmate without the freedom to leave at will. Upon refusing to obey an order to return, two husky orderlies approached him in a menacing manner. Seeking to avoid a scene, the meek and mild man ran out the door. The police were then called in to "apprehend an escaped mental patient." The unaggressive, meek man was forcibly apprehended by the police, who in their ignorance considered him to be a violent maniac. In self-defense against this rough force the meek and mild man became violent. The ignorant police were forced to club him into submission and to place him in a strait-jacket.

The meek and mild man spent the rest of his life violently attempting to escape from the iron bars that encaged

him. He kept screaming madly, "Let me out; I am not insane!" But the insane asylum doctors always responded with an understanding smile. Did not their college text books teach them that a man who thinks he is insane, is not; and that the insane man never claims to being insane? New interns passing by his padded cell were warned, "He is a hopelessly incurable, homicidal maniac." Besides that, the meek maniac still had his original chronic headache.
Thus:

Before starting the cure, beware the calamity.

Treat the sane as insane and you soon treat the insane.

When in quicksand, don't move.

THE KILLER

(On the progressive perversion of moral standards)

A mother was picking fleas off her dog's back. Everytime she caught one she would turn to her little son and say, "Here's how to get rid of them." Then she would crush it between her fingers.

At first the little boy was very squeamish and was sickened by the killing of the fleas. But after a few fleas were killed his feelings became numb and he could observe the killings without the tendency to turn his face away.

After a few more killings the young boy began to look at the details of the crushed flea. After doing this a few times, the crushing and killing of fleas had no more effect on him than the crushing of lifeless peas. Then he began to gleefully, if not sadistically, look for fleas to kill himself. Every time he found one he would rush up to his mother and say triumphantly, "Look, Mommy, I caught another one!" Then he would crush the flea between his tiny little fingers.

After killing fleas it was easier for him to swat and kill flies around the house. After killing flies it became easier to mangle and kill beautiful butterflies. After killing butterflies he found sport in killing birds with stones. Killing birds made it easier for him to decapitate live chickens for the neighbor's Sunday meal. Killing chickens made it much easier for him to get odd jobs of shooting unwanted dogs.

The more he saw warm blood spilt the more cold-blooded

and numb became his feelings, and the more he lost his emotional and sentimental pity, sympathy, and mercy. The more he destroyed life the more contemptuous he became of death.

Killing dogs made it easier for him to stab and kill a man who would not cooperate when being robbed by him. Killing one man made it much easier for him to strangle another man just to prove his strength. Killing two men made it easier for him to club a man to death just for the pleasure involved.

Killing became so easy for this killer, but it was so much easier for the executioner who had killed numberless men. He placed the killer's head under a legal guillotine as coldly as if placing a roll of cold boloney in a meat slicer.

The mother, who used to become nauseated by seeing headless chickens which were killed by her son, went into hysterics in seeing her son's head on the executioner's block. "Why! oh, why did he become a killer," she screamed. She still did not understand why even after she saw her son coldly reach up to crush a fly which was buzzing around his face.

Thus:

Commit a small crime and it is easier to commit a big crime; commit a big crime and it is easier to commit a bigger crime.

Big crimes grow from little crimes.

Evil or good becomes easier each time we do it.

THE THEATER MANAGER

(On perverting disintegration of progressive range standards)

The manager of a theater that seated a hundred people had ten people complain of anti-religious plays.

"Who cares for the minority of ten," he said, "when the majority of ninety do not complain. The customer is always right. To attract the majority of ninety I will make more anti-religious plays."

The ten people who had complained never returned to that theater and the manager never again heard complaints against his anti-religious plays.

Later ten other patrons attacked plays that were anti-patriotic.

"Who cares," said the theater manager, "when eighty patrons do not attack this kind of show. The public demands it so I will make my plays more anti-patriotic to attract more people."

So ten more people never returned to the theater and the manager never again was attacked for his anti-patriotic plays.

Later, ten of the eighty who were left criticized plays that ridiculed political beliefs.

"Who cares," said the theater manager, "when seventy people out of eighty do not criticize. I will make political plays more ridiculous to attract more people."

So ten more people never returned to the theater nor

had reason for criticizing the theater manager about his political plays.

Later ten of the seventy who were left deplored plays that were vulgar and which degraded the sanctity of the home.

"Who cares for the minority," said the manager, "when the majority does not deplore such plays. I give the people what they want. I will make plays more vulgar to attract more of the majority."

So ten more patrons left and never returned to the theater nor had reason to deplore vulgar plays again.

Later the manager realized that he was losing many of his patrons. He had only sixty left. So he said, "Because the majority has demanded more vulgar plays, I will make plays even more vulgar to attract more people."

Ten people criticized the increased vulgarity but the manager answered, "Who cares when the majority of fifty out of sixty demands this vulgarity."

And so it went until only ten people patronized the theater. These were the dregs of society. These were the sensually minded dregs who were left after the complaining spiritually minded and the critical intellectually minded had abandoned the sinking theater. The interest in the theater of these sensual dregs was not artistic. So the manager had to sell peanuts, pop corn, cracker jacks, and soda to maintain a profit. But he lost all these profits in hiring sweepers to clean up the mess and a policeman to control uninhibited riots and vandalism in the theater.

Still the manager, complaining of losing business and the lack of interest in the arts, was heard to say with an ever sickening smile, "The customer is always right. Nine out of ten people favor vulgarity; I will give the public what it demands. I must please the majority, not the minority. To attract more people I will make plays even more vulgar."

Needless to say, the theater soon went out of business and the theater manager went out of his mind.

Thus:

The majority of nine rules and the minority of one weeps as the plurality of ninety sleeps.

Noblemen set standards when kings fail; common men set standards when noblemen fail; morons set standards when common men fail.

The worst at civilization's peak is demanded as the best in its depth.

THE SMOKERS

(On the progressive perversion of moral standards)

"I think it is a crime and moral degeneration for women to be smoking cigarets," said the pessimistic reactionary to the optimistic radical.

"Be broad-minded!" answered the optimistic radical. "Start worrying when you see youth smoking."

A few years later the reactionary again met the radical and in the course of their conversation the worried reactionary said, "It is a crime and moral decadence for youth to be smoking cigarets."

"Be modern!" replied the carefree radical. "Do not worry until you begin to see children smoking cigarets."

Not too many years later the same topic came up between the same two friendly enemies. The concerned reactionary said, "What is this degraded world coming to! It is a crime to see children smoking cigarets!"

"Be tolerant!" said the unconcerned radical. "Let them have their pleasures so long as you do not see babies smoking cigarets."

The years went by and the hair of both men had turned gray, but their opinions were still black and white. The negative reactionary said, "How inhuman! It is a crime to permit babies to smoke cigarets!"

"Be realistic," said the positive radical. "How can it be a crime if everyone is doing it!"

Age had made the reactionary just a little bit more tolerant, so he answered, "I suppose you are right; how can it be a crime if everyone is committing the act? But isn't it a crime and moral degradation the way some women are killing their husbands?"

The radical who had also become more tolerant with age replied, "Be broad-minded! Start worrying when youths begin to kill their parents."

Needless to say, both eventually became broad-minded and tolerant enough to sympathize with unfortunate children who were forced to kill old-fashioned parents. Of course the children were justified, for the parents in most cases attempted to frustrate their attempt to enjoy certain pleasures which these backward parents called crime.

These two men never did give their views on the recent trend for babies to enjoy killing their parents. The reason is that they happened to be killed by babies themselves.

Thus:

Tolerating one crime is the precedent for tolerating greater crimes.

Degeneration is when the evil of one age becomes a pleasure in another.

There are no sinners where there are no saints with which to compare them.

THE PAGAN AND THE PURITAN

(On the progressive perversion of moral standards)

A traveling Puritan whose bus happened to be passing by a public bathing beach was shocked by what he saw there. Turning to the passenger sitting beside him, who happened to be a Pagan, he said in alarm, "How immoral! I can think of nothing worse than wearing a sleeveless swim-suit in public!"

The Pagan laughed at his alarms and said, "Don't be so narrow-minded! I think it is so much more healthy. But I am sure I would protest if no shirts were worn in public."

A few years later the same Puritan and the same Pagan took the same bus trip and passed by the same beach. Again the Puritan was horrified by what he saw there. Again he turned to the Pagan and said in a shocked tone, "How im-modest! Nothing could be worse than to be barechested in public!"

Again the Pagan laughed and said, "Don't be so old-fashioned! I am sure a bare chest allows so much more free-dom of action. But I think that I would protest at any sign of public nudity."

By a strange coincidence the Pagan and the Puritan again passed by the same beach a few years later. The Puri-tan said as was expected, "How vulgar! I have seen every-thing! Nothing could be worse than to permit nudity in public!"

And the Pagan laughed as usual and said, "Don't be a bore! Public nudity is a natural thing to have. Do nude animals think it is so bad? At least nudity is not a hypocritical act which creates a sense of shame and guilt as does clothing."

The Puritan could not repress his indignant rage and burst out with, "So, you can see nothing vulgar in public nudity! Well, neither can you see anything less vulgar or more vulgar. This leaves you nothing left to call immoral, immodest, or vulgar. Neither can you call anything moral, modest, or pure, unless you can find someone wearing a garment to distinguish him from the nude. If you do, then the nude would be immodest and vulgar in comparison. If man is to have civilized social virtues as well as vices, then man must wear clothes—or be like the free, natural, uninhibited dog who has neither vice, virtue, nor civilization."

The Pagan silently wrapped his shell around himself and began to wonder what kind of low species of animal he represented.

Thus:

See no evil and you will see no good.

Nudists with no evil immodesty can have no virtue of modesty.

There is no good or evil without a standard of comparison.

CURI'S ATTRACTION

(On the progressive perversion cycle)

Curi said to his loved one, Ami, "I am so unhappy because I cannot see the strange container that I have heard so much about. I would be so happy if you would only let me see it."

Ami was very willing to oblige her lover so she said, "If it makes you any happier, all right; observe the container."

But Curi was not quite satisfied, so he said, "I am unhappy because I cannot see the hidden details of this container which attracts me so much. I would be so happy if you would but let me see the details."

Again Ami did what she could to please Curi and said, "If it makes you happier, all right; look at the details."

But Curi was still not fully satisfied and said, "I am unhappy because the unknown secrets within this container make it irresistibly attractive. I would be so happy if you would but let me look inside the container."

Ami did not want to disappoint him so she said, "If it will make you happier, all right; look inside the container."

But then Curi looked up in surprised disillusionment and said in an unhappy voice, "Oh! There is nothing in it. This container is so unattractive. I am so unhappy—but look at that strange container over there! It fascinates and attracts me. I am sure it will make me happy."

A disappointed and apprehensive Ami answered, "That

container does not belong to me. I have no other containers to show you. I fear you must remain unhappy, Curi, until you leave me to seek another—to make me unhappy."
Thus:

Get one and we want two; get two and we want three.

Get the greater and we care less for the lesser and seek a greater.

Knowing all stops curiosity's attraction.

THE AFFECTIONATE PEOPLE

*(On the perverting disintegration of
the progressive ranges of society)*

In a little country there once lived a stern, moral, and religious people. In this little country no one would dare do more than wave their hands to express loving affection in public greeting. But in time as morality progressively decreased, the expression of affection progressively increased.

This increased affection was manifested by an immoral few who risked their reputation and even their lives to hold their loved one's hand in public greeting. They had to express a greater love by something greater than a handwave. Of course these ill-reputed, immoral handshakers were condemned and ostracized by the narrow-minded majority. But the tide of lovers' progress could not be stemmed. Soon the entire country was following the once taboo sin of handshaking.

It was not long after when a new generation of young lovers wished to express their greater love to loved ones. They desired something more than a simple handshake which was common among friends as well as lovers. So they dared to hug loved ones in public greeting. Failing to repress this degenerating vulgarity the whole country was soon following the once unusual custom of greeting, not only loved ones but all friends with a hug.

It took radical young lovers to break this odd tradition.

In order to express their greater love for loved ones they began to kiss in public greeting. Of course these radical young lovers were bitterly attacked for their indecent display. But eventually the protesting, reactionary grandparents died. Then the whole country followed the once strange custom of greeting, not only lovers, but friends with a kiss.

Then to express greater affection than friendship, for all friends were kissing each other, young lovers began to hug as well as kiss in public greeting. By now people were more and better educated, more broad-minded; instead of resisting the young lovers they congratulated their original manner of expressing their love. Almost immediately everyone in the entire country began to greet his friend or acquaintance with a hug and kiss.

Beyond this point in the progress of love, originality seems to have died out, for no one, not even the most loved, could think of a greater expression of love in public greeting than the hug and kiss.

Then strange things began to happen: Parents and lovers were displayed no more love than friends and acquaintances. Without this expression of filial and marital love to attract and bind them, lovers and families dissolved. Lovers became unknown, for how could a lover be known without a higher expression of love than that shown his friend. The hug and kiss became such a routine formality that foe as well as friend was hugged and kissed in public greeting. Without the means to express true friendship, friendship soon disappeared. As love withered and disappeared so did friends, lovers, and families—and so did the little country of affectionate people disappear because there were no more affectionate people in it.

Thus:

Love all people to destroy all love.

Love without manifestation is not love.

Show love to an enemy and you show less to a friend.

THE PEACEMAKERS

*(On cumulating cause-effects on
the progressive range of war)*

The caveman bluntly said to his family, "This club will knock the strong brute down to our level and restore peace in the family. Fear of this horrible weapon will prevent future family disturbances."

But not long after, the knifeman made this cutting remark, "This knife will restore tribal peace when it cuts down tyrants who use clubs. Fear of this horrible weapon will prevent future fights between the tribes."

Then a spearman made this piercing statement, "This knife on a pole, a spear, will restore peace within the clan. From a safe distance it will kill tyrants who use knives. Fear of this horrible weapon will prevent future skirmishes between the clans."

But the bowman entered the picture and hissed, "This bent branch and string shoots small spears from a safe distance. With this bow and arrow we will restore peace between the towns by shooting tyrants who use spears. Fear of this horrible weapon will prevent future battles between the towns."

This was so until the gunman barked out, "With this weapon, a gun, we can shoot missiles a greater distance than the bowman. We will restore national peace because from a safe distance we can destroy tyrants who use bows. Fear of this horrible weapon will prevent wars between nations."

And so it was until the bombman explosively burst out, "With this powerful explosive, a bomb, we cannot miss our target. We will restore peace in this civilization by using bombs to wipe out the many tyrants who use guns. Fear of this horrible weapon will prevent future world wars."

But not long after the atomic bombman sneaked in and threatened, "This one atomic bomb, which can obliterate a nation, will destroy all tyrants who use bombs. Then there will be world peace and prosperity. Fear of this horrible weapon will prevent future world annihilation."

Thus it was that Futureman, cringing in his underground atomic bomb shelter, whimpered, "Woe is me! If we fail to find a greater weapon than atomic bombs, then we must suffer the tyranny of those who control atomic bombs. If we do find a greater weapon than atomic bombs, then we must suffer the world's last battle—the Armageddon. Which do we choose if we still have that choice? In seeking peace from war and freedom from tyranny, we have increased the extremes of both. Now we must suffer the extremes of one or the other—extreme peace with extreme tyranny, or extreme war with its resultant extreme freedom of anarchy. Woe is me! But man cannot live without hope. If we are atomigrated then I have hope for the future in the knowledge that when man reaches the bottom, he can only rise— from the dark age caves of clubmen to another bright atomic age of atomic bombmen."

Thus:

A midget with a weapon can be master of a giant.

Every action has a balancing reaction that becomes an action for reaction.

Keep building the tower up and it will suddenly tumble down.

GOD OF THE ANTS

(On perspective of the progressive ranges of nature)

A man, looking down at the ground, saw thousands of ants swarming about many ant colonies. He realized that with one step he could quake or crush a colony. With a few pails of water he could create rivers to drown out many colonies. He could arrange or remove food and soil to cause different ant colonies to go to war. He could easily cause them to run for cover by sprinkling water like rain over them. He was so powerful and the ants were so weak and insignificant. He had the power to control the destiny of individual ants as well as families, groups, or colonies of them. He was a god over the ants.

As his sense of power swelled up within him the sky suddenly darkened, lightning flashed, thunder rolled, and a cloud burst overhead. Covering his head in abject fear he frantically stumbled for protective cover. The god of the ants had fear of his own God.

Thus:

Insignificant ant look up and say, "Insignificant man look up and pray."

The world of ants is the world of man in miniature.

Wise men see nations of men move as common men see colonies of ants move.

THREE MEN AND THREE VIEWS

(On the balanced trinity of perspective perception)

Three men met on the slope of a mountain, and as strangers will when meeting in a wilderness, stopped to converse. One of the men who had been walking up the mountain said, "I have left that dirty, dark, dank, dreary, dismal swamp below. Now I am planning to settle up on that distant high blue hill which looks so clean, clear, crisp, and uncluttered."

Another man who had been walking down the mountain said, "I have left that black, bleak, blighted, burned, and barren hill above to which you were planning to go. I was planning to settle in what seemed to be your gorgeous green grassy ground in the valley. But now I am not so sure of it."

The third man who happened to live on the slope between the swamp and the barren mountain top said, "I have envied you both from here on the slope. To me, the grass looked greener down in the valley and the air seemed clearer up on the mountain. Until today I could never seem to appreciate my home on the slope. But thanks to you two I now realize that the more one studies green grass the more brown weeds he sees, and the more brown weeds he sees the greener look the distant pastures."

Before the group separated to return to their original homes, they all agreed to visit one or the other at least once a year in order to gain a better perspective and appreciation of their own home.

Thus:

Analyze distant beauty and see ugliness close at hand.

Look at your nose and you will not see beyond it; look beyond your nose and you will not see your nose.

The lover sees a halo; the rejected suitor sees a mole.

THE VOTER

(On disintegration of the progressive range of perspective)

Six months before national elections were to be held the conscientious citizen said, "International issues, next year's ten billion foreign loan, and the president of the country will decide my vote."

But time changes all things and three months before the national elections this same citizen thought less of international issues and said, "National issues, the one billion dollar highway construction program, and our national congressmen will decide my vote."

But more time made him more conscious of the issues within his own state so that one month before the elections he no longer talked of national issues but was heard to say, "State issues, the ten million dollar education program, and the governor of this state will decide my vote."

One week before the national elections the candidates for mayor in his city went all out in their campaigns for election. This made the citizen so conscious of the mayor that he soon forgot the governor. As he expressed it in the heat of the mayoralty campaign, "How my city is effected, the one million dollar slum clearance program, and who will be mayor will decide my vote."

This was so until only one day before the election when he was reminded of his tax bill and his children's educational problems at the local school. Very decisively he made up his mind and told his wife, "How our family is going to be effected, the half-million dollar sewer project, and who will be our district council member will decide how I vote."

Then came the great day—election day. The conscientious citizen proudly entered the voting booth to do his duty to his world, his country, his state, his city, his district, and his family. But just as he was about to pull the voting lever he suddenly thought, "What will happen to me personally if I pull this lever? How I will be effected must decide my vote, so I will vote only for those I know personally rather than for the issues they stand for. Maybe I can get that thousand dollar city contract that is still open."

As he walked away from the voting machine the conscientious citizen had a worried look as if his conscience bothered him. He thought, "Did I make the right choice? Did I make a mistake? I wonder if all the opposition candidates were not the better qualified. Well, those who got my vote will certainly not get it in the next election."
Thus:

The longer the time the broader the view; the shorter the time the narrower the view.

See yourself and see not the nation; see the nation and see not yourself.

They who plan on spending millions in the future worry about pennies in the present.

A TRIP TO THE MOON

(On integration of the progressive range of perspective)

"There is my home," said the man as his rocket ship rose from the airport on its way to the moon.

"I cannot see my home," said the man as his rocket ship rose above the city, "but there is my neighborhood."

"I cannot see my neighborhood," said the man as he rose above the state, "but there is my city."

"I cannot see my city," said the man as he rose above his country, "but there is my state."

"I cannot see my state," said the man as he rose above his continent, "but there is my nation."

"I cannot see my nation," said the man as he rose above the hemisphere, "but there is my continent."

"I cannot see my continent," said the man as he rose above the world, "but there is my hemisphere."

"I cannot see my hemisphere," said the man as his rocket approached the airport on the moon, "but there is my world. But has it been worth seeing my world only at the expense of losing sight of my home, my neighborhood, my city, my state, and my country. With a sad note of finality he said, "I feel lonely and homesick."

Thus:

Narrow, specific, concrete facts decrease, in balance, as broad, general, abstract principles increase.

Narrow-minded views increase as broad-minded views decrease.

Increasing loyalty to a broader range of society decreases it for a narrower range; vice versa.

THE LONELY TRAVELER

(On the progressive range perspective of space-time)

A lonely, bitter man had none he could call friend. He had nothing in common with any man, so he hated all men and considered them enemies.

One day he took a long trip to relieve his boring, monotonous loneliness. While in another neighborhood he chanced to meet a stranger who was from his own neighborhood. The lonely man said, "We are from the same neighborhood; we have something in common; let us be friends." So they became friends.

While in another city he met a stranger who was from his own city. "We have something in common," he said, "let us be friends." And so they became friends.

Traveling thru another nation he met a stranger from his own nation and said, "We have something in common; let us be friends." And the two became friends.

Finally on a trip to the moon he met a stranger from earth and said, "We are both from earth; we have something in common; let us be friends." "Yes," said the stranger, "I will be your friend, but is it not strange that here on the moon I consider all from earth as my friends, but on earth I do not even know my own neighbor's name." The other lonely traveler thought a moment and said, "Maybe human fellowship and friendship could be better achieved if we would all imagine that we were on another planet and all men were from our own planet."

Shaking hands in their common agreement of this philosophy, the two entered the local tavern on the moon for a friendly sociable drink. As they passed by a table, two travelers from the planet Mars smiled at them. One of the lonely men said to the other, "Let us sit over here away from those Martian characters; I do not like their looks." The rejected Martians overheard this rude remark and one said to the other, "Maybe universal fellowship and friendship could be achieved if he would only imagine that we were from his own planet."

Thus:

Time and space make friends of enemies.

Few agree on details; many agree on generalities. Few agree with facts; many agree with principles.

Friends see agreements; enemies see disagreements.

THE SEEKER OF KNOWLEDGE

(On disintegration of the progressive range of knowledge)

A renowned philosopher once knew more than any man ever knew about the principles that govern man. He believed that "The more one knows, the less one knows." Still he desired to learn all there was to know of man. His study of man as a whole led to a study of man's body. This led to a detailed study of the arm, which led to a more detailed study of the hand. The more he learned the less he seemed to know so he had to continue his studies. From the study of the hand he went into a more detailed study of the finger, and finally into an infinitely detailed study of the fingernail.

The more he learned of man's arm the more he forgot and the less he knew of man's body. The more he learned of man's hand the more he forgot and the less he knew of man's arm and body. The more he learned of the fingernail the more he forgot and the less he knew of the body, the arm, and the head. As a philosopher he had once written all he knew of the principles of man in one small volume. Now he could not summarize his specialized detailed facts of the fingernail in less than two large volumes.

The more he studied fingernails the more he forgot and the less he knew of man as a whole. Today he is often heard mumbling in a confused sort of way, "The more one knows the less one knows; but I must still seek more knowledge in order to know more."

An ignorant peasant, overhearing this remark, turned to his companion and said, "Why must he seek more knowledge? If he speaks the truth by what he has just said then I am happy to be ignorant, for the less I know the more I must know. If he speaks the truth then why should I destroy what I know by learning more?" His peasant companion, who was even more ignorant, just scratched his head and wondered what kind of homemade brew his comrade had been drinking.

Thus:

See the finger and see not beyond it; see beyond it and see not the finger.

Gain narrow facts and lose broad principles; gain principles and lose facts.

Narrow-minded specialists have a narrow perspective; broad-minded philosophers have a broad perspective; wise men have a flexible broad-narrow range perspective.

THE PHILOSOPHER, STREET CLEANER, AND WISE MAN

(On positive-neutral-negative perspective perception)

A philosopher, a street cleaner, and a wise man sat discussing their activities. The philosopher was well known to be absent-minded for while seeing in his mind he could see nothing with his eyes. By seeing the broad, distant view he tended to lose sight of things close at hand.

The street cleaner on the other hand was more truly the "absent-minded" one for while seeing things with his eyes he could see nothing in his mind. By seeing things close-up he tended to lose sight of distant things.

The wise man who sat between these characters as they conversed was one who likes to keep both feet on the ground and his head out of the clouds. He could look down to see mud at his feet and then look up to see stars in the sky. He was constantly changing his perspective from the abstract broad view to the narrow sensory view.

The philosopher mentioned one of his experiences. "I used to walk the dark streets at night," he said, "with my head held up high in order to see the broad and distant stars. But one night with my thoughts concentrated on the stars I fell into an open sewer with such a splash that I blotted out my starry vision."

The street cleaner laughed at this and added his own experience. "I used to walk the bright streets by day," he said, "with my head held down in order to see the small bits of paper before my eyes. But one day with my eyes concentrated on a piece of paper I bumped my head into a low-hanging branch that made me see starry visions."

The wise man laughed at both and said, "Now that both of you have shared your extreme views, is it not better to realize that you are standing in mud when you look at the stars, or is it better to see only the mud or only the stars?" Thus:

See the leaf and don't see the tree; see the tree and don't see the leaf; change perspective to see both.

Philosophers for broad views; specialists for narrow views; wise men for whole views.

Increase the broad range view, and in balance, the narrow range view decreases; increase the narrow range view to decrease the broad range view.

THE IMITATORS

*(On integration and unity of the
progressive ranges of society)*

One day a passerby was called vile names by a child. He
caught the insolent child and shook him to teach him proper
respect for his elders. But the child, shocked by this unusual
treatment, screamed, "Don't blame me; I only called you
what my father called the mayor."

The indignant man contacted the father and reprimanded him for setting such a poor example for his children.
But the father replied, "Don't blame me; if the mayor can
call the king vile names, so can I. I only imitate the mayor."

The irate man protested to the mayor for setting such a
poor public example to parents. But the mayor answered, "I
set my example by the king; if the king calls his God vile
names, then I am sure I can do the same to the king."

The persistent man had to get to the source of this chain
of bad examples so he approached the king and said, "The
child blames his profanity on the parent he imitates; the
parent blames the mayor he imitates, and the mayor blames
the king he imitates. I say this in all humility and respect,
O King, but are you the source of all the evil profanity that
pervades this land of yours?"

The wise king appreciated this honest, critical report
from one of his people and replied, "I am ashamed to admit
that I am the fountainhead of all the vile evil you have

observed, but it is true. The devil must have possessed me to be profane in public. I cannot blame the Higher One I imitate, for He is perfect and above name-calling. He is my spiritual guide; he is my God. As I will not disrespect and profane my guide, so let me be a guide for my people. Let them look up to me as someone to respect and someone to imitate."

The wise king thanked the satisfied man for enlightening his ignorance. And from that day on the king imitated his God, and was imitated by the mayor, who was imitated by parents, who were imitated by their children. Then it was that disrespect and profanity disappeared from that good land where all respected those they imitated.

Thus:

Imitation is the best teacher of character, good and bad.

As kings act, so act parents; as parents act, so act children.

Civilizations rise when children act like parents and parents act like kings who act like God; civilizations decline when kings act like parents and parents act like children who act like devils.

THE PREACHERS

*(On disintegration of the progressive
ranges of perspective and goals)*

It was a custom of a certain church in England to have
its preachers sum up the basic philosophy to be preached
for the coming century. These were to be written and sealed
in a vault which was not to be opened until the year 2000
A.D.

In the year 2000 A.D. the vault was opened and the con-
tents were published. The first of these reports was written
in the year 1200 A.D. by a mystic theological preacher. He
wrote, "I preach a universal, spiritualistic religion as a
means to achieving spiritual salvation in heaven and to prevent the damnation of the soul in purgatory and in hell. Man
must suffer, do penance, and pray for his soul on earth to
have his sins forgiven and to redeem mankind which is born
evil with original sin. Fear of God's wrath, faith in theological doctrine, meditation, and the conscience are guides to
make man self-conscious and ashamed of his sins and to
develop his stern, unchanging moral character."

In the year 1500 A.D. a more rational philosophical
preacher wrote: "I preach a worldly, humanistic, ethical
religion as a means to achieving happiness in heaven and on
earth. Man must do good deeds on earth and have faith in a
just God if he is to save himself, for man is born with a conscience which tells him what is wrong. His philosophical reasoning, his logical thought, and his ethical principles are

guides to make him conscious of truth, of what is right, and to develop his stable, intellectual personality."

In 1700 A.D. an oratorical political preacher wrote: "I preach a national, patriotic religion as a means to achieving national glory and to prevent national degradation. We achieve this by glorious deeds of patriotism to inspire the nation which is destined to glory under the guidance of God. Legal law, emotional faith in the Fatherland, and the lessons of history are guides to make the nation strong and powerful. These develop proud patriots who are willing to work, fight, and die for our holy cause."

In the year 1800 A.D. a friendly sociological preacher wrote: "I preach a social, non-sectarian religion as a means to achieving group cooperation and brotherhood to avoid social disintegration. We achieve this by eliminating prejudice and discrimination regardless of race, color, creed, or national origin, for all men are created equal and all men are created good. Religious social activity and group cooperation are guides to make our group accept proper attitudes for developing homogeneous interaction."

In the year 1900 A.D. the popular psychological preacher wrote: "I preach an individualistic, scientific religion as a means to achieving individual happiness and material success on earth. We do this by stressing the positive personality and avoiding the negative in all our church social activities. This enables the winning of friends and the influencing of people who are made good or evil by their environment. Scientific laws, statistical surveys, psychological fact, and individual interpretation of these are the guides to eliminate negative self-consciousness. These enable one to know when he is right and to develop his adjustable and ever-changing positive personality."

An unemployed preacher who had no church to go to in the year 2000 A.D. read these reports and said, "After reading this it seems to me that man can no longer satisfy his spiritual needs thru organized religion in this age of excess materialism, sensualism, and lack of intellectualism. So he is going off into the wilderness to find spiritual solace and religion within himself. Materialistic and socialistic churches decay as men become hermits and monks and women become recluses and nuns to find their spiritual God in solitary mysticism. I wonder if that is why there is no need for preachers like me today. Maybe I am the one who needs to be preached to. Maybe I too can find my spiritual God in the silent solitude of the wilderness."

Thus:

Civilizations rise with spiritual religion, peak with intellectual religion, and decline with materialistic religion.

Civilizations rise with a mankind view, peak with a national view, and decline with an individualistic view.

When philosophers who consider all mankind are replaced by psychologists who consider individuals, that civilization is full of narrow-minded people.

THE LADDER OF FEAR

(On relative values of the progressive range of fear)

I feared the bully's beating until fear of disgracing my family honor became greater. I feared disgracing my family honor until fear of disapproval by my social group became greater. I feared my group's disapproval until fear of punishment under the law became greater. I feared punishment under law until fear of the wrath of God became greater. While I fear the wrath of God no one can threaten or force me to do evil, for in fearing the supreme power of God I have no greater fear. Therefore lesser fears hold no threat for me.

Should I lose this fear of God Almighty, the greatest of all fears, then will I fear the law above all. When I lose fear of the law, then will I fear my group above all. When I lose fear of my group, then will I fear disgracing my family. If the day should come when I no longer fear my God, the law, my group, or my parents, then I dreadfully fear that I will have the many fears of the hunted, the persecuted, and the insane.

Thus:

Fears become minor relative to major fears and disappear with greater fears.

Minor fears become major fears when greater fears are lost.

Fear of God brings a fearless peace of mind.

DIVIDE AND CONQUER

(On disintegration of the progressive range of goals)

A mighty emperor was once asked how he managed to acquire most of the civilized world without using great armies to conquer nations or to maintain those already conquered. "It is simple," he said, "for as a nation is composed of individuals, so is a civilization composed of nations. I simply divide to conquer. I divide a civilization into its nations and disintegrate the nation into groups; then I divide the groups into individuals. I accomplish this by first degrading respect for religion and moral law, for these are the elements that unify a civilization. Then I degrade and destroy patriotism and constitutional law, for these are the elements that unify the states of a nation. Then I degrade and destroy loyalty to majority groups by propagandizing anti-discrimination of minority groups. Finally I disintegrate individuals from remaining groups by stressing the all-importance of individualism and equality. My experience has proved that the latter is best accomplished thru the public schools and thru the culturally weakened intellectuals of the nation. Thus I disintegrate a civilization into elements by degrading and destroying the spiritual goals that unite them. Without these spiritual goals of religion, patriotism, and loyalty to integrate their spiritual, mental, and physical activity, individuals turn to the material and sensual goals of money and pleasure. Outside of these they have no other reason for being, no other reason for working, fighting, and dying if need. Then I leave the individuals to dissipate, degrade, and destroy themselves. When material and sensual goals become all-important then I know they will not fight and die for the spiritual goals of group loyalty, national patriotism, or religious piety. After the whole has been disintegrated into its parts then it requires only a small minority of my well-organized agents to become the majority party in government. They do so quite easily for no one else can unite the self-interested individuals to participate in becoming a majority party. My agents then apply the free political system of the nation to deliver the nation to me—without a battle and without the loss of a life."

The emperor concluded by saying, "I do not conquer nations, I liberate and revive sick, corrupt, and dying nations. To maintain these liberated nations without armies I simply return what I had removed. I unify the nation by restoring parental respect, family honor, group loyalty, national patriotism, and religious faith. Then the conquered will fight and die to maintain my government, for I have given them other spiritual goals to work for, to fight for, and if need be to die for."

Thus:

Destroy the highway and roads become useless; destroy the roads and byroads become useless; destroy the byroads and destroy social man.

Common goals integrate the varied many; uncommon goals disintegrate the united many.

Individualism unites none; politics unites few; patriotism unites many; religion unites most.

THE KING AND THE CITIZENS

(On the progressive cyclical change of authority)

Once upon a time a king declared to his serfs, "My humble serfs, by divine right do I rule."

And his servile serfs answered, "O most noble king, we would die for thee."

Later the king told his subjects, "My subjects, by royal decree do I rule."

And his subservient subjects answered, "O royal king, we would gladly fight for thee."

Still later the king decreed to his people, "My people, by the power invested in me do I rule."

And his patriotic people answered, "O King, if you but command, we will do battle for you."

And still later the king announced to the citizens, "Citizens, with the consent of parliament do I rule."

And the critical citizens answered, "Yes, King, let parliament agree before we fight for thee."

Time passed by and the king said to his fellow citizens, "Fellow citizens, I rule only as the people wish."

And the fickle fellow citizens answered, "Remember that, King, before signing any declarations of war."

Then the time had come when the king pleaded with his friends, "Friends, the nation crumbles; I beg your help."

And the murderous mob answered, "Be quiet, fool; whom do you think you rule!"

Thus:

When kings degrade to citizens, citizens degrade to mobs.

As kings change, so change their subjects; as subjects change, so change their king.

Common men will die for noble men, but laugh at common kings.

THE SUPERIOR-INFERIORS

(On distribution of the superior-inferior balance)

The wise man said to the genius who had just boasted of his supreme intellect, "You may be superior to some, but no one can be more superior than the Supreme Being."

"God is my superior," answered the genius, "but this average man is my inferior in intellect."

"That's all right," said the average man, "you may be my superior in intellect, Genius, but the moron is my inferior."

"The average man may be my superior in intellect," muttered the moron, "but I cannot complain for I am superior to the idiot."

The idiot accepted this fact, for as he said it, "The moron may be my superior in intellect but my pet dog is probably my inferior."

"I am near the bottom on the scale of intellect," said the dog, "but I can still claim to be a lot more superior than that stupid worm."

The lowly worm said, "So help me, I must be superior to something." Then as he burrowed lower into the ground he squeaked, "Excuse me, but I am still looking for my inferior."

Meanwhile, all the younger, radical worms had developed inferiority complexes and were planning a campaign to eliminate such feeling of inferiority by a universal campaign to have children educated. They were to be taught

the doctrine that not only all worms were created equal but
so were all dogs and men created equal.
Thus:

We are not superior or inferior; we are superior-inferiors
—superior to some and inferior to others.

The superior artist may be an inferior plumber; the superior plumber may be an inferior artist.

Superiority is relative to time, place, individual, circumstance, and degree.

THE EQUALIZED IDIOT AND THE GENIUS

(On the progressive range of superiority)

Down in the tavern a number of men were quenching their thirst and fraternizing with each other. After a few beers their well-oiled tongues began to loosen. One of the men, an average-type fellow, had feelings of inferiority brought on by his beers and by the witty talk around him. Turning to a well-known genius he slurred, "Don't you know that all men are created equal in this society? What makes you geniuses think that you are so superior to us average men? Are we supposed to be your inferiors?"

Maybe it was to avoid an argument, but the genius replied, "Since no one is inferior in this society, we geniuses will not be abnormal. We will strive to act like you average men."

But a moron who was hanging on to the bar felt that what was good for the average man was also good for the moron. He bellowed, "So, if all men are created equal, who do you average men think you are to be acting so superior? Do you think we morons are your inferiors?"

He was a huge moron and his hamlike fists convinced the average man to say, "Oh, excuse me, no one is inferior in this society. We average men will act like you morons to prove that we do not think we are superior to you."

An idiot who had drunk himself under the table whimpered, "As you said, all men are created equal in this society. But why are we idiots discriminated against as being inferior by you so-called superior morons. Don't you believe in equality for all?"

The idiot's whiskey tears softened the moron's heart and in all sympathy he said, "Of course we believe that all men are created equal. No one has the right to call himself superior or to call another inferior. I think you misunderstood us when you thought that we morons were acting superior to you idiots. We will act like you idiots just to prove to you that we are not superior to you."

This emancipation proclamation sobered the idiot, and crawling out from under the table he said jubilantly, "What a wonderful achievement in social progress! We have finally achieved what man has always sought. Now we are all equal; now we are all idiots. Oh, wonderful day!"

A sub-idiot who had just staggered in from the gutter outside heard this and said in a challenging tone, "Don't be so sure of yourself, Idiot! I think you really believe that you are more superior than we sub-idiots. What makes you think we are so inferior to you? Are not all men created equal and are not we sub-idiots like men, too?"

Before an answer could be given they all passed into an equal state of unconsciousness. For it seems that the bartender was afraid that they would all make him agree to being equal and make him act like an idiot. He thought, "Well, I would be an idiot if I agreed to that." So to save his own meager brains and sanity he gave them all a free drink. This was his favorite drink, called "Idiot's Delight," so none refused the favor. They did not know that it contained a knock-out pill.

Now truly all men were created equal—unconsciously so—except the smug, superior bartender who drank a toast to his superiority by gulping an "Idiot's Delight." But of course, he forgot that he had put one of the equalizing pills in it.

Thus:

Genius can equalize down to idiot level, but idiots cannot equalize up to genius level.

A nation striving for social equality strives for national idiocy.

Civilizations rise with high-class aristocracy, peak with middle-class republicanism, and decline with low-class democracy.

THE WISE AVERAGE MORON

(On the distribution balance of superiority-inferiority)

An average young man moved to a strange city. There he had no friends, belonged to no group, and found it difficult to meet acquaintances. Lonely and unhappy he said to himself, "I am so lonely and unhappy. I must find a friend or a group to belong to. I must be recognized by someone. I must find my place in this world."

He approached a fellow employee on the job and attempted to initiate friendly relations. But this employee was some sort of a mental genius and rebuffed the friendly youth with, "I think you are so dull and uninteresting. You must avoid associating with me unless you desire to be my subordinate servant."

The average youth resented this remark by the genius even tho he knew it to be true, even tho he knew he had nothing in common with the genius. "Woe is me," he said, "I am so lonely and unhappy. I feel so miserable. I feel so inferior. The genius has rejected me. I must find some other person or group which is more on the average level that I am on."

He approached an older worker who appeared to be an average person. But the youth's maneuvers to gain a friend made the older worker suspicious of the youth so that he said aggressively, "You may think you are as smart as I am, but remember this, we are both competing for the same

goals. One of us will become master; one will become servant. I will do my best to make sure it is not I; so watch out
for yourself."

The average youth was surprised by this aggressive
reception to his friendly overtures. "Woe is me," he said, "I
am now so confused and even more unhappy now. I have
been rejected by an average person who is so antagonistic. I
don't want to fight him. I want to be friends. Where can I
find a friend or a group which will be friendly toward me?"

He could not stay on the job with the average older man
always glaring at him aggressively so he quit and found
employment elsewhere. Here he met a high-grade moron
who was always smiling and appeared to be quite friendly.
He knew he had finally found what he had always been
seeking when the mild moron said, "You are so much
brighter than I am. Won't you be my friend, my counselor,
and my leader; I will be as a servant to you and treat you as
a wise master. Let me introduce you to some of my moron
friends first."

The average youth finally achieved recognition from
others; he had achieved a feeling of belonging and a feeling
of superiority. No longer was he lonely and unhappy; he had
found his place in the world. The average youth had become
a wise man among morons. He had become a wise average
moron.

Thus:

A moron is a fool among geniuses but a wise man among
idiots.

The lamp is dull relative to a brighter lamp but bright
relative to a duller lamp.

The child is not born into his destined place; he must find
it in his youth.

THE ADJUSTMENT

(On disintegration of standards on the self-discipline cycle)

The hardworking king was over-fatigued from carrying out his royal responsibilities to his people. He called on his psychiatric adviser and said to him, "I feel tense and nervous; what do you advise I should do?"

The psychiatrist expressed the latest opinion on the subject when he said, "Your Majesty, you fight and resist the nobleman too hard. You must relax and release your inhibitions before they explode. You must act less like a king and discard your tense formal manners which require inhibiting self-control and self-discipline. You must adjust to your prevailing situation and environment. You must adjust to the less formal level of the nobleman."

A short time later the king again called for his psychiatric adviser and on the royal couch he confessed, "I have adjusted to the nobleman's level, but now we both feel tense and nervous. We always argue and can never agree on how we should handle the common man. What shall we do?"

The psychiatrist referred to the latest text on the subject and said to the king, "Sir, you and the nobleman are fighting and resisting the common man too hard. You both must relax and release your inhibitions. You both must act less like noblemen and discard your inhibiting formal noble manners. You both must adjust to your situation and environment. You must adjust to the informal level of the common man."

The king did this, but only became worse. So he saw the psychiatrist again and said, "The nobleman and I both adjusted to the common man's level; now we all feel tense and nervous, including the common man. Now we all argue and can never agree on how to handle each other. What can we all do about it?"

The psychiatrist, after looking up the latest theory on the subject said, "King, all of you are fighting and resisting the complexities of this declining nation too hard and too seriously. You all must learn to relax and to release your inhibitions. You all must adjust to your situation and environment. If things are becoming barbaric, then adjust and be barbaric. Now the latest theory proves that the caveman had no such thing as insanity. Therefore we should all discard any formal manners which still make us inhibited and tense. We must adjust to the informality of the caveman if we wish to avoid insanity."

Later the king sat on a rock in his cave, scratched his back with his club, and said to himself, "Learning is a wonderful thing. I must commend the wise psychiatrist for his expert knowledge. I am no longer tense and nervous, but neither am I king. Now there are no tense and nervous noblemen and common men, nor are there any psychiatrists; but of course, there are no such people in our society now. We have no such thing as social inequalities to cause emotional and mental problems. Now we are all equalized and well-adjusted cavemen who have no superiors. So obviously this has done away with mental problems involving superiority and inferiority complexes. Yes, it is amazing and wonderful how psychiatry has relaxed and adjusted us."

But life in a cave tended to be lonely, and the king, who was of a sociable nature, wanted someone to talk to. So he went over to see the local witch doctor.

The local witch doctor was the former psychiatrist who

had adjusted to his situation and environment. After hearing the king's complaints he chanted his magic hocus-pocus and abracadabra which was beyond the comprehension of normal mortals. It was known only to those initiated into the inner sanctum of witch doctors. The magic words went something like this: "The subject is a schizophrenic dual personality, manifested by oedipus and electra complexes aggravated by syndromes of anxiety psychoneurosis, disassociating the subconscious id and ego, and complicated by melancholia. Psychoanalytical catharsis is mandatory."

The effect on the caveman was soothing and relaxing, for the magic words sounded as if the witch doctor had a magic communication with the sacred spirits. But the real cure came when the witch doctor suddenly screamed, threw dung dust in the man's face, and jabbed him deeply with a pin. This was the famous shock treatment which the witch doctor had picked up at the last meeting of the professional association of witch doctors. The shock treatment was effective, for the caveman rushed out a cured man. He had to be unless he wanted more of the same treatment. He would get his sympathy and someone to talk to elsewhere. Thus:

Civilizations rise on prohibition, peak with inhibition, and decline with exhibition.

Rulers prohibit; noblemen inhibit; common men exhibit.

When angels degrade to the devil's level, they say they adjust.

ALL MEN ARE CREATED EQUAL

(On disintegration of the progressive ranges of superiority)

When a king was in distress he had the humility and wisdom to seek the advice of others. Calling a conference of the leading authorities in his land to assist him in solving a problem, he said, "I rule the best I can, but even so, I am distressed by citizens being incited to revolt by demagogues. These agitators preach the doctrine that all men are created equal. Now I have called this council of professors to determine whether or not all men are actually created equal. If all men are equal, then I, as a good king, will strive to be no better than the peasant. What is the opinion of you wise men?"

The mystic referring to his abstract symbols and signs declared, "All men are created equal in the eyes of God. God equally judges the rich and the poor, the good and the evil, according to universal and eternal revelations."

The philosopher referring to logical syllogisms and theorems reasoned thus, "I agree but only in degree, for all men are created equal in the eyes of Nature. Nature's lightning bolts equally strike the rich and the poor, the good and the evil, according to the universal and eternal principles that maintain the balance of nature."

The historian referring to his charts and chronologies stated, "Let us be realistic and abide by the lessons of history that have really occurred, not by abstract theories. Let us realize that all men are created equal in the eyes of political law. This law equally judges the rich and the poor, the good and the evil, according to the seldom changing national law of the land."

The sociologist referring to the quotation of authority and to stacks of statistics said, "I will prove that the other professors have been too vague and general in their opinions. Now figures do not lie, and to quote the latest authority: Nine out of ten sociologists now believe that all men are created equal. This then means that the rich and the poor, the good and the evil, all deserve equal treatment. This is in accordance with this recent statistical survey which may be changed when a more recent poll is completed."

The psychologist referring to experiments conducted on a complex control board gave his opinion. "Let me point out that no knowledge can be called truth unless proven by experiment. That is why the psychologist speaks the greatest truth in saying that all men are created equal in the eyes of the psychologist. We psychologists have determined that the rich and the poor, and the so-called good and the so-called evil, are equal descendants of monkeys. And like any other species of animal men and women equally have bestial sexual desires that should not be inhibited if insanity is to be prevented. This is in accordance with experiments conducted on dogs yesterday, which, of course, refutes the experiments conducted on mice the day before. This is our own school of thought so it may be contradicted by other psychological schools of thought."

The king, appearing to be confused, interjected, "After listening to you profound wise men I am a bit confused as to the equality of man and of beasts. Let me ask the floor sweeper if he thinks that all men are created equal."

The floor sweeper, resting unconcernedly on his broom handle, overlooked the indignant glares of the professors and said, "Well, sir, that should not be too difficult to answer. To be sure, if all men were created equal, you would not be king nor I a sweeper. If all men were created equal, all would be kings and none would be sweepers. You would not be big, strong, intelligent, and blue-eyed, nor would I be small, weak, dull, and brown-eyed. To be sure, if all men were created mentally equal your wise scholars would not have so many different and unequal ideas, nor could they have any ideas on equality if all were equal."

The king meditated for a moment and then said, "Those are wise words, not of one equal to a professor, but of one greater. From now on you will be my adviser and my advisers will be my floor sweepers. If these floor-sweeping professors complain of their lowered position and dignity, then I will know them to be hypocrites who talk of equality for all men but resent being equalized to a lower status themselves."

Thus:

All men will be created equal when all men are born idiots.

Idiots cannot equalize to act like geniuses but geniuses can equalize to act like idiots.

Nations degrade when kings equalize to common man level.

THE BROTHERHOOD OF MAN

(On disintegration of the progressive range of goals)

Once upon a time all the people of a country were happily united and without conflict. This was because they all had the common moral values of their common religion—all except one because he did not like his priest's looks. And of course, not belonging, he felt like an outcast. Being alone he had no one to express his atheistic views to, so he became a neurotic reformer to express his views to the world. He would not change to accept the moral standards of the country, so he would get the country to accept his standards. The church had prejudged him to be antagonistic to the faith and his indiscriminate attacks against others made others discriminate against him. So the reformer justifiably said, "Religion causes intolerant prejudice and discrimination against free-thinkers. Away with all religious bigotry! Let us have a tolerant brotherhood of man. Away with all religions!"

So piety and devout love of religion were done away with.

But the people had to have a spiritual love for something greater than themselves in order to give them a reason for being and to unite them into a cooperative group. As they lost their religious devotion they found a greater patriotic love for their country. But the neurotic reformer's hard, cold heart would not tolerate the warm and inspiring emotion of patriotism. Instead of reforming himself he went out to reform the country of the evils of patriotism. In one of his many attacks on patriotism he said, "Emotional patriotism causes intolerant prejudice and discrimination of other nations. Away with biased, nationalistic patriotism! Let us have a tolerant brotherhood of man where all men love each other."

So national allegiance and patriotic love of country were done away with.

When patriotism was no longer a cause to work, fight, and die for, men became fraternal and joined with other men of common interests to unite into social groups. The radical reformer's disposition was such that no group would have him in fear that his agitation would disintegrate the united group. Again, instead of tolerating and not discriminating against such social groups the reformer, who was truly and rightfully discriminated against by these groups, began to preach, "Snobbish social and political group loyalty causes intolerant prejudice and discrimination against minority social groups. Away with such selfish group loyalty! Let us have a tolerant brotherhood of man where there are no majorities to discriminate against minorities!"

So loyalty and fraternal love were done away with.

About the only social group left in that disintegrating country, by which a man could find a common interest and have common goals and values to inspire cooperation and the practice of virtue, was his own family. But the cranky, uncooperative, but influential reformer was ostracized and discriminated against by his neighbors for his lack of cooperation and virtue. So he went out to destroy families which practiced the horrible crime of discrimination. Speaking at a mass rally of frustrated spinsters and bachelors he shouted, "By loving one's family to a greater degree than other families indicates intolerant prejudice and discrimination against those families who are loved less. Away with such bigoted family love! Let us have tolerant brotherhood, let us not discriminate by loving one more than another!"

So paternal, maternal, and filial love were done away with.

Not long after, all men lived without love, had no common goals to enable cooperation, had no means to practice virtue, had no one to work, fight, and die for, and had no reason for being. Many ended their being as a result, but those who did not lived in silent solitude, for they had no reason for loving or living with others. One of these, in the meditation that comes with solitude, had a sudden revelation of truth and its consequences. Groaning miserably, he expressed this revelation in words to himself, "What have we done! We have done away with devotion, patriotism, loyalty, and love of mother. Now all are equal and none discriminates against another. All are like equal brothers, so none is loved more than another. Now there is no bias, no bigotry, no prejudice, and no discrimination. Oh, Miserable man! Now there is no society. Now there are only hermits without loyalty or piety."

The reformer who felt rather superior at his accomplishments went about looking for someone to praise him. Seeing the miserable lonely man he said, "Isn't it wonderful now that we no longer have prejudice and discrimination in our society."

The sad and miserable hermit screamed in insane rage, 'You monster! You have destroyed everything and everyone for being prejudiced and discriminating. But why! Oh, why did not someone realize before this that you were the most biased, the most bigoted, the most prejudiced, and the most discriminating of all in attacking and destroying religious devotion, national patriotism, group loyalty, and family ties. You destroyed all as being bigoted, so let me destroy you, you bigoted beast."

Before the surprised reformer could say, "You are biased and bigoted," he was garroted.

Thus:

Tolerance that is good becomes evil when it cannot discriminate between devil and saint.

Increase love for your neighbor's child, and in balance, you decrease it for your own.

Increase tolerance for one thing, and in balance, we decrease it for another.

PATRIOT'S DAY

(On the value balance of the progressive range of society)

A traveler returned to a country he had previously visited and was amazed at the changes that had taken place. In discussing this with a friend on a national holiday, called Patriot's Day, he said, "When I visited this country twenty-five years ago I was thrilled by the dynamic enthusiasm and inspired by the proud patriotism displayed on Patriot's Day. On that glorious day of honor to heroic patriots I was blinded by the flashing of national flags, deafened by the crackle of exploding fireworks, and exhilarated by the laughing gaiety of children and adults. I was awed by grand parades, with proud soldiers marching to stirring military bands that blared inspiring patriotic music. Every home, factory, and business place had a national flag conspicuously waving in the breeze. Every child proudly and enthusiastically waved his flag on high as the parade passed by. I was impressed by seeing all stand erect to salute the national flag passing in review. My emotions were stirred by orators who pledged their solemn allegiance and praised the glory of patriots who had fought and died for their beloved motherland. It was an inspiration to see so many people so moved by the fervor of the occasion that weeping was not uncommon. I said to myself on that day, twenty-five years ago, this is a people that is spiritually united behind its motherland. I predicted then that this country would make great progress to be the envy of the world. But now I feel my predictions were wrong."

"Why do you say that?" said his friend, "I feel we have made tremendous progress in the last twenty-five years."

The traveler answered sadly, "I say this because today, on this same Patriot's Day, twenty-five years later, everything seems to have a sickly mood and a deathly silence about it. I see no flags and no parades. I hear no exploding fireworks, no patriotic oratory, no laughter of children. I see and hear no masses of people united as one in celebrating a common glory. There is no sound, no fury, no life. What caused this horrible sickening and death of the once stirring and inspiring vitality of Patriot's Day?"

His friend laughed and scoffed, "Are you really as concerned as you sound? You sound like a real old-fashioned flag-waver! Times have changed. We now believe the individual is the most important element in our society. Unfortunately, a few years ago one of these individuals, a child, was injured by his careless handling of fireworks. Because of this we have banned all fireworks for all people in order to protect the individual's safety. Was not that a wonderful indication of social progress and the advancement of individual freedom and liberty? Just think, a whole nation has been willing to forfeit its right to have fireworks in order to protect one individual. Unfortunately thousands of adults lost their jobs and probably a few committed suicide as a result, but the others soon got over it. And as for fun on Patriot's Day, well, a day at the beach has taken its place. But because some children drown each Patriot's Day, we are seriously considering the closing of all public beaches on this day. By doing this we may save a few lives. After all, the pleasure of many individuals is not worth the life of one. In fact, last year a man was killed on Patriot's Day by a meteorite that fell out of the sky. As a result, many people are demanding that for the protection of the individual all individuals must remain indoors on Patriot's Day. Yes, sir, we in this country can be proud of our progress in considering the individual's rights as being the most important element in our society."

The perplexed visitor did not know what to say, so he said in agreement, "Yes, it is truly remarkable when the right of one individual can cause fifty million individuals to relinquish their common right." He began to feel a little sick as he again surveyed the sickly mood and deathly silence of a nation that was spiritually dead—cause of death, deterioration from lack of patriotism.

Thus:

There are family, group, government, and religious rights as well as individual rights.

Fight for individual rights and you fight against group rights; fight for group rights and you fight against individual rights.

In giving a right, a law represses a right; in giving a freedom, a law imposes a tyranny.

THE RIGHT TO WORK

(On progressively cumulating a perversion cycle)

A wise man speaking to a group of workers celebrating the national holiday of Labor Day summarized the gains made by labor: "We have attained order and stability in our society," he said, "because the family, as foundation of our society, is stable. Women's place is in the home; the husband is the breadwinner. We labor only forty hours a week and have leisure for fun, contemplation and creative work. We respect the Sabbath as a day of worship and of rest. We have laws to prevent the exploitation of child labor. We have improved our wages, hours, and conditions. We have ended slavery and created the dignity of labor and the respected worker. We have struggled, fought, suffered, and died to achieve these freedoms and benefits for labor."

One of the workers in the audience was heard to say grimly, "Woe to those who would destroy these freedoms to enslave us! I will fight and die to save these freedoms and benefits!"

But it was not too long after when this same worker was heard to say, "I must improve my standard of living. I demand that we be permitted to work fifty hours a week. Then I will have the money to buy the finer things in life."

The wise man, upon hearing this, gave a warning, "Beware! Your extra wealth will compete for the finer things. Prices will rise. You will soon be working fifty hours a week to buy what you once did after a forty hour week."

But soon the worker's wife became dissatisfied because her neighbor had a new car and she did not. She complained, "My husband cannot maintain our finer status on his pay. I demand the right to work forty hours a week in order to support my family."

Again the wise man heard and again he warned sternly, "Beware! Your extra wealth will compete for what you will buy. Prices will rise. You and your husband will soon be working ninety hours a week to buy what your husband once bought after forty hours work."

But the worker's child had grown. He was sixteen years old. He was unhappy and could not study in school, for as he said, "My mother and father cannot support me. I need money to buy what I enjoy. I need an automobile like the Jones boy has. I demand, and my parents support me on this demand, that I have the right to work forty hours a week in order to support myself and my parents."

The wise man upon hearing these demands warned glumly, "Beware! Prices will rise. Your family will soon be working 130 hours to buy what your father once bought after forty hours of work."

But the worker and his family were too busy enjoying the finer things in life to bother with such gloomy predictions. But then it happened. The worker began to demand of his labor union. "Our family cannot support itself," he said, "we must work on Saturdays and Sundays if we are not to lose the finer things in life that we have gained. Let us do away with this ridiculous and impractical Sabbath law. I demand the right to work on Sunday as well as Saturday."

The wise man, who happened to be at that meeting, turned to the demanding worker and bitterly repeated the worker's own words from his past, "Woe to those who would destroy these freedoms to enslave us! Now who will fight and die to save these freedoms and benefits?"

Thus:

Free man is free to destroy his freedom.

Freedom is fought for, but given away freely.

Busy labor demands idle leisure; idle leisure demands busy labor.

THE BETTER GOVERNMENT

(On balancing of self-disciplined moderation)

The republicans ruled and the democrats weeped until demagogues ranted and the intellectuals demanded, "The self-disciplined responsibility required in the republic stifles our freedom. We need more freedom to do as we please. We need a better form of government. We need a democracy where free people will rule and restore individual rights and freedoms."

So democracy was achieved by revolution of the masses, who ousted and deposed the ruling classes. Freedom from discipline became freedom controlled by self-discipline, which turned to freedom with license, and finally to the freedom of anarchy. Now man was free to murder, but most men were not free to leave the safety of their homes in fear of the few murderers who practiced their freedom. So these fearful, good people demanded, "We have the anarchy of excess and undisciplined freedom. We need to control this democratic anarchy. We need a better form of government. We need an autocracy where a strong leader will rule and restore individual responsibilities and duties."

So the disciplined class overthrew the undisciplined mass and appointed a dictator to dictate the laws of the land. For the good of the nation individual rights and freedoms were replaced by national duties and responsibilities. It wasn't long before the lazy, the leisurely, and the irrespon-

sible began to demand, "We have the tyranny and discipline of excess law. We need freedom from this slavery. We
need a better form of government. We demand a democracy
where free people will rule and restore individual rights and
freedoms." But those who still recalled the anarchy of democracy made counter-demands, "Hang the radical democrats
for advocating anarchy and the violent overthrow of law and
order!" There were also a few old-timers who could still
remember the distant past when the republic reigned. They
had lived under three governments and felt a responsibility
to express their evaluation of all three.

One of the former republicans expressed the philosophy
of self-disciplined moderation that was the basis of the republic: "We have had the undisciplined anarchy of excess
freedom and the disciplined tyranny of excess law. Each was
demanded by citizens; each was achieved by revolution;
each was a reaction to the actions of its forbears. Maybe we
need a degree of both tyranny and anarchy to counterbalance and neutralize the bad effects of each. Maybe we need
self-disciplined responsibility and rule by representatives to
control the authority of tyrants and the anarchy of the
masses. Maybe we need self-disciplined moderation to control freedom within the limits of excess and deficiency.
Maybe both freedom and rights are needed to counterbalance and neutralize responsibilities and duties. Maybe we
need a better form of government, like a republic."

The self-disciplined public agreed and revolted to oust
the ruling class and repress the clamoring mass. And the
republic did turn out to be one of moderation between the
extremes of anarchy and tyranny. But in every republic, no
matter how good, there will always be malcontents or idealists, depending upon who describes them. Besides the controlling majority of self-disciplined moderates, there was a
left wing minority seeking undisciplined, democratic anarchy, and a right wing minority seeking disciplined, aristocratic autocracy. When the self-disciplined moderates failed

to self-control themselves or to control the anarchists, it was not long before the disease spread contagiously and the majority began to demand, "We have need for more freedom and rights. We need a better government. We need a democracy. . . ."

And when this excess freedom became anarchy, others demanded, "We need more responsibilities and duties. We need a new form of government. We need an autocracy. . . ." Thus:

Freedom is a point of moderation between anarchy and tyranny.

The government of a people is what they demand and deserve.

When self-discipline becomes undisciplined, discipline is demanded.

THE PROGRESS OF GOVERNMENT

(On disintegration of progressive ranges of government)

In a certain civilization that was rising out of the ruins of its dark age, the king expressed the sentiments of his nobles when he said, "I do not like the way the religious pope of the church rules by moral law. Let us progress to a better system of royal government where the king of each nation makes the laws."

This was achieved but the nobleman became dissatisfied and expressed the feelings of the merchants when he said, "I do not like the royal king of the nation ruling by ethical law. Let us progress to a better system of representative government where the appointed noble representatives of the people make the laws."

This was accomplished but the merchant spoke for the common man when he said, "I do not like the aristocratic noblemen of the upper house of parliament ruling by legal law. Let us progress to a better system of republican government where selected representatives of the common people make the laws."

This was done but the common man speaking for the non-voting masses said, "I do not like the way the selected common men of the lower house of parliament rule by social law. Let us progress to a democratic form of government where the elected common people make their own laws."

And so it was, but then one citizen speaking for the many said, "I do not like anarchy where every man rules by his own laws. Maybe that is why our civilization is declining and disintegrating. So let us progress to a better system of religious government and moral law where religious leaders rule."

Thus:

Every government fought against was once a government fought for.

Moral law integrates all; ethical law integrates many; legal law integrates few; individual law disintegrates.

Civilizations rise on moral law, peak with ethical law, and decline on legal law.

THE SEASONS OF LIFE

(On constant balancing cyclical change of perspective)

Three members of a family, a grandfather, a father, and his son, lived in the same house. And as is not unusual under such conditions there were family arguments. During one of these arguments the young son who was just out of college said, "I cannot understand why the aged are so cranky and morbid. Life is full of fun, adventure, and beauty. I am active in sports which build up my healthy body. I dance, flirt, and court with beautiful girls. I have fun at school, marriage, engagement, and wedding parties of my many school friends. I am optimistic and inspired with hope and prepare for a bright future of success, leisure, and pleasure."

The middle-aged father who was pretty well settled down with married life said, "I cannot understand why youth is so worry-free and the aged are so worried. Life is full of problems but they are dull and boring. All I do is stay home to relax my tired body after a hard day's work by having a beer in front of my TV. I fight and argue with my nagging wife, yell at my children, and attend dull christening and wedding anniversary parties with the few scattered friends I have left. I feel apathetic, cynical, and indifferent about the future as I prepare for a dull future of security and retirement."

The aged grandfather who had long since retired said, "Well, I cannot understand why youth is so wild and carefree and the middle-aged are so indifferent. Life is full of sorrow and bitterness. All I do is stay home to squint at TV with my failing eyesight and care for my garden and my aching and painfully sick body. I spend hours with my rare friends praising the past and condemning the present. Or I visit them when sick and attend wakes and funerals to meet former friends. I feel pessimistic and depressed and have no hope, except an increasing religious hope, as I prepare for a dark, useless, and miserable future of surviving as long as I can."

One of the grandfather's old friends, who was old in body but young in spirit and wise in mind, happened to be in the house. To pacify the difference of opinion he said, "Man never seems to learn that life is determined to constantly change from birth to living and dying. Life is a whole made up of many parts which man self-determines, such as birth, flirtation, courtship, marriage, christenings and anniversaries. As the seasons of the year determine a man's activities and viewpoint, so do the seasons of his life determine his activities and his viewpoint. And to all of us, the joy at birth is predetermined to become the sorrow at death." Thus:

The sorrow at death is balanced against the joys at birth.

Every year and every life has its spring joys, summer boredom, and winter misery.

It is determined that man shall self-determine his predetermined life.

THE PERVERSION CYCLE

(On changing cause-effects of the perversion cycle)

"I think we live to be as happy as we can," said the bright young student to the wise old teacher.

"Yes, my son," replied the gray-haired scholar, "that is true. But shall we say the flower is happiest under constant, bright, warm sunshine? Shall we say the flower is saddest under constant cold, dark rain? Or shall we say the flower constantly worries about withering under burning, never-ending sunshine, or drowning in the misery of never-ending rain? Shall we say the flower appreciates the happiness of bright sunshine only because it has the misery of dark rain with which to compare it? Can we have a good without evil with which to compare it? Can we have happiness without sadness? Can we have pleasure without misery? I say to you, my son, on the balance scale of life, if you must have your pleasure, then you must also balance it with misery."

"But how can that be," said the inquiring student, "when everyone knows pleasure to be good in itself?"

"My son," said the wise man, "it is pleasure to eat, but does not the misery of a painful stomach balance the degree of gluttony? It is a pleasure to play, but does not the misery of aching muscles balance the degree of excess playing? Can we truthfully say that eating and playing are pleasures? Or are they miseries, when excess causes both pleasure and misery?"

"I begin to understand, sir," said the attentive student, "but what is the significance of such knowledge in the over-all plan of life?"

"Let me tell you of a man," said the wise teacher, "a man born into *hardship* and *misery*. He was happy to eat stale bread—when he could find it. He sought greater happiness and pleasure in life. These goals called for *self-disciplined effort* which enabled him to achieve and to eat fresh bread— but stale bread no longer made him happy. His *efforts* brought him *success* and greater happiness, for now he could eat cake—but stale bread and fresh bread no longer made him happy. His *success* gave him the *leisure* to contemplate and try the finer things in life. So he became happy in the *pleasure* of eating pie—but stale bread, fresh bread, and cake no longer made him happy. He soon *dissipated* his happiness for pie by eating it to excess, so that the unhappiness of boredom set in.

"In seeking further happiness and pleasure, he tried anything for a change and soon found greater happiness in eating creampuffs—but stale bread, fresh bread, cake, and pie no longer made him happy. By this time he had tasted all the pleasures there were—nothing could satisfy his taste or make him happy.

"But as a progressive 'educated' individual, he now sought happiness in change—and began to experiment with *degrading* perversion as a pleasure. This soon caused a dis-illusioned, apathetic, and cynical contempt for all pleasures. Nothing in the present gave him pleasure, and he had no goals or hopes of future happiness.

"As he had lost all taste for pleasure, the finer foods of his cultured, refined, and delicate tastes softened his body, weakened his mind, *dissipated* his spirit and emptied his pockets. He was *ruined*. Because he could no longer pay for further pleasures, and because of his progressive loss of will-power to reject perverting pleasures, he could make no *self-disciplined effort* to maintain what he had achieved. So he lost everything until once again he found happiness in eating stale bread as a matter of *survival*. And once again he had everything to gain and nothing to lose. He once again had many goals and hopes of future *pleasure* and happiness to spur his dynamic, *self-disciplined efforts* and activity. So you see, my son," concluded the wise man, "*pleasure* begets misery, and misery begets *pleasure*."

With a nod of understanding, the now wiser student answered, "Yes, Oh, wise man, I now perceive that to have the greatest *pleasure* and happiness is to do without some *pleasure*."

"Yes, my son," replied the wise old man, "remember this guiding rule: *Self-disciplined* moderation, between the extremes of excess and deficiency, brings the better happiness."

Being a conscientious disciple of the learned philosopher, and truly believing what he had been taught that day, the student went out and got himself half-drunk that night, not fully drunk as he had originally planned. He did this to forget the extremely difficult examination the learned professor had planned for his class the next day.

Thus:

Pleasure begets misery; misery begets pleasure.

Self-disciplined moderation between the extremes of excess and deficiency brings the better happiness.

Survival, hardship, self-discipline, effort, success, leisure, pleasure, dissipation, degradation, ruin, and return to survival are progressive phases in the lives of the individual, family, group, city, nation, and civilization.

UP AND DOWN WITH THE JONESES

(Changing standards on the self-discipline cycle)

John Smith and James Jones were born on the slummy side of the superhighway. Living outside the zones of social pressure, they were as free and uninhibited as animals. Neither had ambitions to rise above their bare survival conditions. They were friendly, cooperative, non-competing neighbors. Or so they were until the day Jones straightened up and beamed with pride and elation for having successfully achieved his goal. He had taken a rare bath and suffered the hardship of washing his tattered clothing.

Smith, observing Jones strutting before his ramshackle shack thought, "Jones must think he's better than I am; look at him putting on his fine manners! He's reeking with moral character, self-discipline, and determination to do better than I. Well, he's no better than I. I can keep up with Jones anytime!"

Jones was startled by the unusual cleaning activity at Smith's shack. Never had he seen such driving effort. He also became conscious of the change in Smith's character and appearance. The grim look of accepting a challenge hardened his face as he thought, "Smith is becoming as clean as I am. He's acquiring as many fine manners and becoming as strong in self-disciplined character as I. Who does he think he is—an aristocratic nobleman! I'll have to keep one step ahead of him by developing even finer manners and character. I'll not have him boast of being more successful and superior than I. I'll move to a bigger and better house."

Smith, keeping an eye on Jones as a standard to compare his own improvement, perceived the improvement in Jones who now had a four-room home and a more dignified character. As the spirit of competition welled up in him he thought, "Jones thinks he can keep ahead of me, but believe me, he's no better than I. I can keep up with Jones anytime. He's not my equal! I'll show him how superior, intelligent, and successful I am!"

He too acquired a better house of six rooms, a better character, and better clothing to symbolize his superior rank in society. He also acquired a college degree to prove his intellectual superiority and success over Jones.

In his new eight-room residence Jones became almost frantic over his own bustling activity and driving efforts. Was all this competitive activity worth it? "I'm at my wit's end," he said, "trying to find ways and means to prove my manners, my character, and my education are superior and more successful than Smith's. My formal manners have become so complex and so controlling that I have little free will of my own left. I must change my pattern and make myself different from Smith. I'll prove that I have my own free will and am a personality quite different from him. I won't compete with Smith; I'll use my leisure time to develop my own personal culture and personality."

From his own eight-room residence in the suburbs Smith saw the personality changes in Jones and felt that he had gone far enough in letting Jones determine how he should act. "I'll be damned if I'm going to act like he's acting! After all, I have my own mind and my own personality. Jones has become such a hypocrite with his artificial personality; I refuse to follow his example. My personality can be better than his; let him copy me if he wants to enjoy my pleasures."

Adjusting the tight collar of his formal tuxedo suit, Smith began to practice smiling before a mirror to show his teeth. After all, the grim face of character and the sober face of dignity did not make for popularity.

As Jones realized that there were a greater number of visitors entering the Smith residence he pondered philosophically, "Smith seems to be more popular than I; maybe if I relaxed my formal manners a little and moved out of this stifling neighborhood I can become as popular as he. Maybe a little dissipating pleasure once in a while might do me some good."

Adjusting the loose tie on his conservative business suit, Jones practiced laughing before his mirror. His merry laugh would be more popular than Smith's frozen smile.

Smith moved close to Jones and was not to be outdone. The neighborhood became alive with pleasure-seeking social callers at both their mansions in the country. Behind his toothful, popular smile and gay manners Smith was concerned. "Jones," he said, "is becoming as popular as I since he dropped his hypocritical formal manners and etiquette. Maybe if I dropped a few more of my aristocratic manners and became more republican, and if I moved back to an eight-room house among more common men, I too can become more popular."

Adjusting the collar of his open-neck sport shirt he began practicing the use of cuss words. He would have no common man saying he talked like a superior snob. He would be more democratic and popular than that superior snob, Jones. And those superior snobs who gossiped about his degradation just were not keeping up with the times.

Jones was not to be outwitted and underranked by his neighbor. "He thinks he's clever," he thought, "but I can be just as democratic and popular as he. I'll move to that four-room cottage near the superhighway. There I won't have to be concerned about my drinking buddies raising hell."

Rolling up the cuffs of his dungaree work pants he

practiced snarling out of the corner of his mouth. He would show that Smith that he was less of a superior snob than he. He would show all his friends that he was their equal, not their superior.

This competition for inferiority continued until both Smith and Jones became as free and uninhibited as they were when they lived in shacks. In fact they did live in their ruined shacks once again. They had chased each other down the ladder up which they had chased each other. Now that they were at the bottom again they glared silently at each other thru the dirty windows of their lonely shacks. Their tattered clothing, and the bodies within them, had not been washed in months. They were both weary of the competition of keeping up and down with each other. Now they settled down to stagnate, atrophy, and survive as best they could on the memories of their glorious past. Thus:

Man rises with character, peaks with personality, and declines with popularity.

Man rises as he strives for formal manners and declines as he strives for informal manners.

Man rises as he strives for superiority and declines as he strives for inferiority.

DYNASTIC PORTRAITS

*(Progressive change of man's nature
on the self-discipline cycle)*

An art gallery recently displayed the portraits of a famous dynasty of kings. The portraits were placed in chronological order and each could be described as follows:

Otto I (The Lion-Hearted): He portrays hard, unsmiling moral character and a powerful strength of spirit, mind, and body which have been molded by use. His stern, sober, determined look indicates one who has SURVIVED HARDSHIP and has no LEISURE time for unnecessary adventure or PLEASURE. Symbols of his strength and authority are seen in the heavy battle-axe held in his strong hand; in the dark, unornamented battle armor on his muscular body; and in the solid battle helmet on his erect head. A heroic, masculine, and martial man was he.

Otto II (The conqueror): He portrays dynamic, tight-lipped determination and the active use of body and mind which have been scarred by battle. His determined, adventurous look indicates one whose SELF-DISCIPLINE and tireless EFFORTS enabled him to conquer all. He, too, had no LEISURE time for PLEASURE. Symbols of his power and SUCCESS are seen in the long battle-sword in his muscular hand; in the glittering, ornamental battle-armor on his lean, hard body; and in the royal crown-helmet on his firm head. A brave, manly soldier was he.

Otto III (The Wise): He portrays scholarly, smiling wisdom and a calm, relaxed body and mind which have been softened by education. His soft, serene look indicates one with no need to conquer; one with much LEISURE time to contemplate ideals as well as culture and PLEAS-URES. Symbols of his wisdom and reign are seen in the light scepter in his soft, bejeweled hand; in the rich royal robes on his sleek, soft body; and in the gold crown on his bent, soft head. A cultured, intellectual idealist was he.

Otto IV (The Fat): He portrays gay, laughing PLEAS-URE and a fat weakness of body and mind that have atro-phied from disuse. His weak smile and haughty look indi-cate one who is flattered for gifts, not praised for deeds, and who has no time to conquer or to contemplate, but too much time to DISSIPATE in PLEASURE. Symbols of his PLEASURE and position are seen in the delicate flower in his white, effeminate fingers; in the ornate silks, ruffles, and jewels on his plump body; and in the jewel-crusted cap on his tired-looking, double-chinned head. A weak, effeminate courtier was he.

Otto V (The Pig): He portrays a face that is molded by evil greed and the flaccid indifference of having DISSI-PATED in perverting and DEGRADING PLEASURES. His nose turns up as tho smelling his own reeking perfume. His fat pomposity goes with the bloated body and distorted mind of one who wallows in his own DEGRADATION and apathetically awaits his own RUIN. Symbols of his DISSI-PATION and DEGRADATION are seen in his gaudy gar-ments; in glittering jewels on his bloated body; in hands too effeminate and weak to hold anything, let alone sword or scepter; in long, manicured finger-nails that would break at the least bit of work; in pale, painted face that sees moon-light more than sunlight; and in an effeminate hair-do that attempts to restore youth to a vice-lined face. A DISSI-PATED, DEGRADED, and degenerate devil was he.

Incidentally, Otto the V (The Pig) was overthrown by

a young leader who can be described by the same SELF-DISCIPLINED traits as was Otto I (The Lion-Hearted). Thus:

Change the mind to change the body; change the body to change the mind.

Change a man's character and he will change his clothes.

In principle, individuals, families, groups, cities, nations, and civilizations follow a self-discipline cycle of: survival, hardship, self-discipline, effort, success, leisure, pleasure, dissipation, degradation, ruin, and return to survival.

THE MISERABLE SLAVES

*(On balancing change of the civilization
self-discipline cycle)*

In the year 500 B.C., a suffering Roman slave was heard to complain, "Oh, how we miserable Persian and Roman slaves are oppressed in this golden age of our Greek masters. But let my master dissipate and degrade himself in leisure and pleasure; I will strive to upgrade myself with self-discipline and effort to replace him."

500 years later, in the year 1 B.C., a persecuted Byzantium slave was heard crying out, "Oh, how we miserable Greek and Byzantium slaves are exploited in this golden age of our Roman masters. But as my master begins to degrade himself in luxury and culture, I will upgrade myself by stern self-control and determination to replace him."

500 years later, in the year 500 A.D., an abused Saracen slave was heard to wail, "Oh, how we miserable Roman and Saracen slaves are discriminated against in this golden age of our Byzantium masters. But my master begins to act like me; I shall begin to act like my master. Maybe this will make me his master."

500 years later, in the year 1000 A.D., a distressed Western man was heard to denounce, "Oh, how we miserable Byzantium and Western slaves are shown such intolerance in this golden age of our Saracen masters. But let them soften their bodies with pleasure and their minds with edu-

cation and culture; I shall harden my body with work and my mind with plans to replace my master."

Sometime after this a confused Western man was heard to say, "Is this the golden age of our Western civilization? Is this our thousand year opportunity to benefit by the historical lessons of past civilizations? Oh, well! In the leisure and pleasure of this golden age, let us forget such gloomy talk. Let us close our minds to such ideas and not tolerate these pestering prophets of gloom and doom. For hundreds of years we have been morbid pessimists who worried too much about the lessons of past history; now let us eat, drink, and be merry optimists. Let us make and write contemporary history as we prepare for a bright happy future."

Thus:

The past oppressed become the future oppressors.

As one nation or civilization declines another rises to replace it.

Gay drinkers laugh at lessons taught by fallen drunkards.

THE TOWERS IN THE VALLEY

(On cumulating cause-effects of the self-discipline cycle)

Once upon a time there was a deep, dark, narrow valley. Within this valley there lived a strange breed of people whose civilization revolved around building tall, thin towers to reach the bright, warm sun. They built these towers slowly for they were resisted and discouraged by their reactionary elders who had vague, unproven, superstitious fears about building tall towers. Any radical who sought to change this slow building pace, or who attempted to speed up the pace of progress, was sentenced to be tossed from the tallest tower in the valley to his death below. So it is understandable why for many years the reactionaries were many, radicals were few, and progress was slow when it should have been rapid. But such slow change produced a stable society that tended to develop strong characters who built strong towers that could last for ages.

Eventually, however, a time came when there were many tower tops being warmed by the bright sun. Within these warm towers were warmed many people. The fact that the towers were completed meant that there was much more time for leisure, contemplation, and creative experimentation. This enabled the middle-aged, moderate conservatives to assume control of the building of towers. These conservatives, while not discouraging the building of more towers, feared that towers built too fast and too high would topple too soon. They also feared that too many tall towers would shade the warm sun from older, smaller towers. These moderate, conservative middle-agers were attacked for such ideas by elder reactionaries who wanted no more towers, and by younger radicals who wanted to build as fast and as tall as they could.

In time, however, contemplative leisure in the sun became boring. Many young radicals appeared and began to make themselves known. They were looking for a change— any kind of change so long as it relieved the idle monotony of their conservative, stable society. When change should have been resisted in order to maintain what had been gained, the radicals assisted in creating revolutionary changes. Of course they were resisted by reactionaries and conservatives, but progress progressed. Soon the radicals would resist the reactionaries and the conservatives.

Assuming control of tower building the radicals built towers taller and faster and faster and taller. Then one day there was no wealth left with which to build more towers; in fact, there was no wealth left to maintain what had been built. The towers they had built were not very strong, for they had been built for the present, not for the future. So it wasn't long before the newest and tallest towers toppled and tumbled. They fell on smaller towers that toppled and tumbled on smaller towers. Soon not a tower was left standing in the valley. All in the valley was now in total darkness and ruin.

Those radicals who had survived this tragic catastrophe lived in a dark valley that saw no warm sunshine. Uniting to survive, they solemnly pledged to resist all change. They vowed to be reactionary and to resist and destroy all radicals who would bring such dark ages of doom and gloom to the valley.

But already one of the children of these survivors began to be bored with living in unchanging darkness and ruin. He began to have strange and radical ideas about building tall, thin towers that would some day reach the warm sun. He could not understand why the elders in the valley were so superstitiously set against such obviously beneficial ideas. But he did not speak these ideas aloud, for he feared the penalty of being tossed from the highest ruins in the valley to his death below.

Thus:

When civilizations rise, change is resisted when it should be assisted; when civilizations decline, change is assisted when it should be resisted.

There is no action without a balancing reaction, nor radical without a reactionary.

Moderation between the extremes of deficiency and excess is better.

THE PHILOSOPHICAL BUGS

(On the balancing cycle of perspective)

A certain species of bug had a life span of three months. This span of life was the cause of many literary disputes among the buggy intelligentsia. One wise, old, scholarly bug had lived to the ripe old age of three months. He had spent his entire life acquiring the knowledge and wisdom of experience. He felt he was well-qualified by his experience to teach the younger generation of bugs. He wrote a book which summed up his life-time of learning. This book became a best seller and the source of a new educational theory to be experimented with on youngsters in school. He taught the youngsters this philosophy: "You must smile and be positive. Burn up all the old books that now warp your little minds in saying that life is a matter of concern and survival. Life is all a bright, warm, sunny, fruitful summer. Adjust yourselves to live a life that is carefree and gay in a world of pleasure. You must accentuate the positive and eliminate the negative from your life."

The well-educated younger generation was reared on this worry-free philosophy of pleasure. They were not prepared and they were ignorant of how to adjust to the winter season that was soon upon them. They suffered miserably and froze to death in the middle ages of their lives. A few of the fittest bugs managed to survive that bitter winter. One of these, after his full life of three months, wrote a book on his death bed. He wanted to pass on the sage wisdom of his bitter experience to the younger generation. He wrote: "You must be stern and negative. Burn the books of those who warp your minds with a philosophy of pleasure. Life is all a dark, cold, stormy, and barren winter. Adjust yourselves to be sober and stern in a world of self-survival. Accentuate the negative and eliminate the positive."

But this learned younger generation soon found itself in the balmy warmth of spring. They all had the stern, sober, and self-disciplined character which enables one to survive the hardship of winter. But they lacked the relaxed and carefree disposition which enables one to enjoy the pleasures of spring. One of these frustrated bugs bitterly and regretfully wrote a book in his old age of three months. With the indisputable evidence of his life-long experience he demanded that books teaching character and survival be burned as warping the minds of the naive and the young. With all the authority of his old age he wrote, "Life was made to be optimistic and positive. Life was made to be enjoyed." So all gloomy and pessimistic books on survival were burned as being superstitious nonsense. The younger generation needed no encouragement to be optimistic and to enjoy the gay pleasures of life.

But there was one old bug whose strange, peaceful, and silent manners made other bugs suspicious of him. Their mockery of him forced him to live the life of an eccentric hermit high upon a secluded rock. He was an old bug. In fact, one modern, well-educated young bug who could boast of being an authority because of his college pedigree, was heard to jeeringly and sneeringly say, "He must be at least twelve months old, which of course is impossible. But regardless, his age has withered his mind as well as his body." This brilliant scholar continued, "His senile, demented mind can conjure up the craziest, most fantastic ideas. He is crazy enough to think that life is not all spring weather.

In fact, he has a fantastic idea that everything in life constantly changes. Isn't that ridiculous? I have to laugh at his mystic mumbo-jumbo which seems to say that the weather changes every three months out of every twelve. He claims that it follows in the order of a warm spring, hot summer, cool autumn, and cold winter, and then repeats itself. Ho! Ho! Ho! How fantastic can he be!" This talkative bug was then seen to walk away with his antenna stuck up in the air as if to broadcast, "How superior can we be!"

Naturally this crazy hermit never bothered to write a book, for if he had, he, as well as his book, would have been burned out of existence. Because his ideas were such fantastic distortions of truth maybe it is just as well that no one ever bothered to listen to him explain them. He died the next winter and his strange ideas died with him. He died just as the starving, freezing, radical, bug-brained new intelligentsia was demanding the burning of books on the previous positive philosophy of summer pleasure.
Thus:

The experience of one age creates the philosophy of the next.

Time, like space, refutes the experience of the living.

Only old age and broad history can perceive the cycles of man and nature.

THE FREE SPEAKERS

(On self-disciplined moderation of the freedom balance)

The radical, young revolutionary practiced his free speech when he said, "We have lost our right to speak against the government; we must revolt to gain this right of free speech!"

He was answered by the conservative old rulers who retorted, "We cannot tolerate free speech by those who advocate the violent destruction of law, order, and our society. We must repress the radicals' free speech to repress their revolt."

But the revolution came just the same. The conservatives were defeated as the radicals succeeded. "We have won the revolt," said the radicals who were fast becoming conservative to conserve their gains. "We have gained our right to free speech. We must suppress and destroy any who would advocate the destruction of this free speech."

So the former radicals freely expressed and the former conservatives were forcibly suppressed. The conservatives who were now radical in seeking reform complained, "You have destroyed our right to speak freely against free speech. Must we revolt to gain this right to speak freely?"

The former radical reformers who were now conservative rulers answered this charge bluntly, "Watch your speech, you irresponsible radicals; we cannot tolerate such free speech in those who advocate the violent destruction of free speech and of our society."

But free speech controlled by self-discipline soon became free speech without discipline. Such words as sacrilege, profanity, obscenity, libel, and slander, lost their meaning and disappeared, for they described nothing in this land of complete free speech. This was a land where all spoke freely except those who would speak against free speech.

So the radicals, seeking to gain their right of free speech, revolted against the conservatives and their right of free speech.
Thus:

The poor who denounce the rich may become rich and be denounced by the poor.

Radicals who denounce conservatives may become conservatives and denounce radicals.

Free speech without self-discipline is like a ship without a steersman—both destroy themselves.

THE OPTIMISTIC PESSIMIST

(On moderation of the optimist-pessimist balance)

Once upon a time in the days before television eliminated the social visit and the art of conversation a family
gathered together to discuss things in general. The elderly
grandfather had just finished making some dire predictions
concerning current events. The impulsive elder son, a freshman in college and knowing all the answers said, "I hate
pessimistic reactionaries with their gloomy views. These
prophets of doom and gloom see everything thru dark
glasses. We all know that times are getting better. We now
have bigger and better houses, schools, and churches. We
now have more money, more cars, and more luxuries. All
these indicate to me that we will have a better future. I
resent pessimists who try to depress me in the present and
who destroy my hope for the future."

The confused younger son, still in high school and quick
to pick up radical ideas said, "I think my brother is right.
We need a positive outlook on life. 'Keep smiling,' that's my
motto."

The grandfather felt he had to give his younger grandson the facts of life. And in rebuff to the elder grandson
he said, "I pity optimistic radicals with their cheerful views.
These predictors of cheer and eliminators of fear see everything thru rosy glasses. We all know that times are getting
worse. Homes are disintegrating, education is deteriorat-

ing, religion is degrading, and patriotism has long been lost. Vice, violence, and vandalism are obviously increasing. This to me indicates a worse future. I feel sorry for the optimist who in not admitting these problems cannot prevent their getting worse."

The grandson looked depressed as he said, "That is such a negative outlook on life; it makes me feel so morbid."

"Now just a minute," said the boys' father, "before we get into an argument let me explain my viewpoint. The optimistic and the pessimistic view are both right even tho they both predict contradictory futures. That is because they both see opposite sides of the same coin. The optimist sees an increase in the quantity of material things; the pessimist sees a decrease in the quality of spiritual things. But as I see it, as quantity increases, quality decreases. As material things increase, spiritual values decrease. So the pessimist is right when he says things are getting worse—they are, in spiritual values. So is the optimist right when he says things are getting better—they are, in material things. Therefore, I, as an optimistic pessimist, like to feel that both the optimist and the pessimist are necessary and right; yet both are wrong in their extremes. One is needed just as much as the other to counterbalance the other." Thus:

As quantity increases, in balance, quality decreases; as material values increase, spiritual values decrease.

Without pessimists there would be no optimists.

It takes two different people to see two sides of the same coin at the same time.

THE DRINKER OF HAPPINESS

(On moderation of the happiness balance)

Observing others to be happy and laughing gayly whenever they drank liquor, an unhappy man sought to find
happiness in liquor himself. He reasoned thus: "The more
liquor I drink the happier I will be." He found that his reasoning was correct, for he became rapturously and highly
ecstatic on the liquor until he passed out into blank unconsciousness. Next morning the painful and lowly miseries of
a hangover, and the shame over what he had said and done
while drunk, made him swear to prevent such degrading
misery by drinking less.

He drank less and truly found less dark misery, but he
also found less bright happiness. He still felt depressed after
the happiness of his drinking. To prevent this depression he
swore he would drink only to get the elation of good drink
and good companionship. But this pleasant elation was still
balanced by the deflation of unpleasant afterthoughts. To
avoid such unhappy deflation he resolved he would have
only one drink in order to feel mellow and rosy whenever
he felt sour and blue. He did this and found that he had
achieved a state of easy contentment, even if it also meant
being a bit moody at times. Thinking that this contentment
was achieved by stopping most of his liquor, he thought he
could arrive at a happier state by stopping all liquor. He
did this. Now he had reached a strange state that was

neither ecstatic nor miserable, happy nor depressed, elated nor deflated, pleasant nor unpleasant, rosy nor blue, contented nor moody. In fact, he realized with a sudden shock that without contrasting emotions he was like the walking dead—he was like a zombie. Unfortunately the shock was so great that he returned to alcohol in excess and lived depressively ever after.

Thus:

Ecstasy balances misery; happiness balances sadness; elation balances deflation; positive balances negative.

We cannot fall without rising; the higher we rise the farther we fall.

Self-disciplined moderation between extremes of deficiency and excess is better.

THE SEEKER OF HAPPINESS

(On relative values of the progressive range of happiness)

A young man, isolated in the deep valley of a wide mountain range, considered himself happy as a hillbilly. One day a magazine fell from a passing airplane and landed before his ramshackle shack. The ragged, barefooted hillbilly retrieved the magazine, the first he had ever seen, and was transformed by what he saw within.

He saw handsome men and beautiful women in fine clothing, living in magnificent mansions, and eating luxurious delicacies. Everyone in the magazine, especially in the advertisements, had the happiest faces he had ever seen.

The ignorant hillbilly never realized he was so unhappy until he compared his happiness with those in the magazine. His bliss of ignorance faded, and in gloomy introspection he was prepared to perceive all the faults that made him unhappy. He brooded over these faults and as his list increased so did his misery. Compared with those in the magazine, he was the most unhappy person in the world with all his faults.

But he was an intelligent ignoramus and it occurred to him that he should balance his negative outlook with a more positive perspective. So he balanced his positive blessings against his negative troubles to neutralize them. He concluded from this evaluation that he had more to be happy about than to be sorry for. This restored some of his original happiness.

But life in the neon-lighted cities beyond the mountains, where even the grass looked greener, still intrigued and beckoned him. Could he be happier over there? He began to seek reasons to justify his going to the city. What would he be like in twenty years? He brooded over this question and became unhappy as the negative emotions from fear of the unknown painted a dark picture in his mind.

He snapped out of this dreary brooding with the realization that it was wise to look ahead for rivers on the highways of life, but it was foolish to worry about crossing these rivers until they were reached.

The unhappy hillbilly decided his life's goal would be to seek and find happiness. So bidding goodbye to his home and family he went over the mountain to see what he could see.

Before he left, a friend who had made several trips to the general store in the distant village warned him, "Beware of those city slickers; they are wicked, deceiving, and not to be trusted."

With innocent ignorance the seeker of happiness accepted this gossip as truth. He placed a defensive attitude about himself to keep untrustworthy city slickers at a safe distance. He prepared for their deceitful hypocrisy by looking for faults in all he met. He saw all the faults he was prepared to perceive—even those not there. He blinded himself to virtue and good intentions by seeing bad motives behind all good deeds.

Naturally, all he met reacted to his defensive-aggressive nature by setting up their own defenses in fear of him. In self-defense they made life miserable for him as they expected he would make it for them. The Seeker of Happiness found it very difficult to find happiness.

He met a fellow hillbilly from his own state, and with this common element to unite them, they became friends.

In comparing notes the fellow-statesman thought city folk were wonderful, trustworthy people who wanted only to help strangers in trouble. This was just as his father had told him it would be.

This contradiction caused the hillbilly to reconsider his attitude and to make the following conclusion: Two people see the same stranger; one sees a halo; the other sees horns. So each must perceive what he has been prepared to perceive. One sees happiness; the other sees unhappiness.

The Seeker of Happiness decided the best means to be happy was to imitate the happy. Seeing a man laughing he inquired, "What makes you so happy?"

"Who's happy!" laughed the man, "I'm so miserable I can't stop this hysterical laughter."

Seeing a woman crying he asked, "Can you tell me what makes you so unhappy so I can avoid it?"

"Who's unhappy!" she sobbed, "I'm so happy I can't help crying."

Obviously, concluded the confused Seeker of Happiness, we cannot imitate others to find happiness. And as great happiness weeps and great sorrow laughs, happiness and sorrow must be parts of the same unified entity. They must differ only in degree from a standard of comparison.

He had a general impression that preachers were sad and judges were solemn, while clowns were gay and widows were merry. His investigation revealed the preacher and judge considered themselves to be very happy. They manifested sadness and solemnity as best befitting their dignified positions. The clown was a miserable grouch behind his gay mask, while the widow's merry smile concealed acid bitterness. Her mask of merriment was to attract potential husbands.

Apparently, decided the Seeker of Happiness, the manifestation of happiness is relative to the individual's position and goals.

He heard that most people enjoyed athletic sports, so he

joined the crowd at a sports event. There he observed that victors manifested the positive emotions of happiness, but losers manifested the negative emotions of unhappiness. When the score was evened, both sides manifested the neutral emotions of conflict and confusion.

He did not know which team won the event but he did know that achievement elates and makes for happiness; frustration deflates and makes for unhappiness, while conflict confuses and makes for neither happiness nor unhappiness.

For the same reason, he went to a theater to observe the audience rather than the stage. He noticed many in the audience laughing happily and crying sadly in unison with the actors. If one person applauded happily, all contagiously applauded, even those whose faces expressed no appreciation. If no one initiated applause, no one applauded.

It seems, reflected the Seeker, that happiness is contagious and cumulative in its effect, and unhappy people will manifest happiness if they believe their social group expects it.

The next day he heard a laborer singing happily in the rain as he shoveled knee-deep in cold, wet mud. The thought of being happy while doing such cold, dirty work almost nauseated the Seeker. But he was still rational enough to conclude that one man's happy work is another man's chore and bore.

The Seeker of Happiness envied the physical strength, the beautiful voice, and the obvious happiness of the singing laborer. Lacking these superior qualities himself he felt inferior and unhappy. He sought to find some fault in the man he envied, some means to knock him off his superior pedestal. But his attention was distracted by the mumblings of a crippled idiot begging alms. Immediately he had a sense of physical and mental superiority that made him feel rather happy. His happiness made him generous with his alms to the begging idiot.

As he walked on, beaming at his own generosity, he

phrased a moral to be gained by the incident: Compare with superiors to feel inferior and unhappy; compare with inferiors to feel superior and happy.

As he tried to forget the superior, singing laborer it occurred to him that he had prepared to find fault and to do all he could to deflate the superior laborer to his own level of inferiority. The incident being closed, and reason having replaced his emotional ego, The Seeker made this conclusion: The happy are envied by the less happy who make efforts to destroy this happiness. So paradoxically, happiness makes for unhappiness. This didn't sound right to the Seeker, but he accepted it as truth when he found nothing to deny it.

After standing in the cold wind and rain to watch the happy laborer, the Seeker sought a restaurant. A hot cup of coffee before a roaring fireplace would make him the happiest man in the world.

As he waited for his coffee a man in his undershirt came in dripping with sweat. "Whew!" he ejaculated, "I've never seen it so hot in that furnace room! A nice cold drink while sitting on a cake of ice would make me the happiest man in the world. Give me the coldest beer you got!"

The Seeker shivered as he saw the frosted beer bottle. Hugging his hot mug of coffee to his chattering teeth he stated another principle of happiness to himself: One man's nectar is another man's poison. One man's happiness is another man's unhappiness.

He overheard one diner say to another, "I have never heard of a man who loved a woman as much as he."

"Yes," agreed the other, "but have you ever heard of a man who hated a woman as much as the one who divorced her?"

The conversation faded as the Seeker of Happiness added this truth to his knowledge of happiness: A woman is not necessarily the source of a man's happiness, for one man's love may be another man's hate.

He observed a carefree soldier laughing and joking with

a delighted waitress. In the booth beside them sat an old man reading a book, oblivious to the gayety about him. He appeared so sober and unhappy that the Seeker intruded upon his solitude to ask, "Why is that young couple so much happier than you?"

"Who is to say who is happier?" replied the old man in a perturbed tone. "If I appear sober and serious it does not mean I am unhappy. Maybe it means I am cynical of the sham behind most manifestations of happiness except those having to do with intellectual happiness. Happiness means tranquility of mind. Those two are like children. Children and fools lead merry lives for they cannot see future difficulties lying beyond their present actions. They have the ignorance that is bliss. In happy ignorance they cannot foresee the consequences that lead to unhappiness. Those two may appear to be happier than a pessimistic predictor, but in long range perspective they will find less happiness. For his hour of pleasure, our soldier friend may suffer a life-time of misery. Those who are not ignorant can foresee and prepare for eventualities. Only knowledge gained from books can enable the preparation for future happiness. Take it from me, son, all happiness can be gained by reading; no happiness can be lost by it."

These seemed like persuasive arguments to the Seeker, but being a good scholar by now, he wanted to see the other side of the same coin. He asked the soldier what he thought of his happiness at that moment as compared with the old man's.

"Well," said the soldier giving the waitress a playful tap on the cheek, "it's obvious that I'm happier than that unhappy, dried-up-looking old man. Happiness to me means the excitement and thrills I feel thru my senses. I experience and feel my happiness, not dream and imagine it. What kind of real happiness could he possibly find in his books? Can he kiss the girls in his books as I can in my experience?"

With that he abruptly proved his point by kissing the surprised waitress on the lips. Then he returned to his more pleasant conversation with the happy waitress.

The Seeker of Happiness returned to his cold coffee to resolve some kind of principle out of all this when he glanced out the window and observed a group of stern-looking religious preachers preparing to attract passersby for a sermon. From past experience he knew they would preach against sensual happiness, and against the happiness of free-will thinking. They would preach the happiness that is peace of soul and which is gained only by faith and belief.

With these thoughts still in his mind, the Seeker formulated these general principles of happiness: What makes one man happy has another man's contempt. Ignorance is bliss to many; wisdom is happiness to others, and faith is ecstasy to some. This indicated there was not just happiness, but three kinds of happiness—spiritual, intellectual, and sensual happiness. And from the way the different people acted about the restaurant he concluded that one cannot have all three happinesses at the same time, for as one of these happinesses increased there was a balancing decrease in the others.

He left the restaurant as a parade came down the street. He stood beside a mother who beamed with the happiness of pride as she watched her children watching the parade. In the parade a baton-twirler strutted in the happy pride of ability; men marched in the happy pride of their group, and on-lookers smiled with patriotic pride at symbols of their country's glory.

Feeling proud and happy at his keen observation, the Seeker expressed another lesson in happiness: Pride in oneself, and in one's family, group, and nation is a source of happiness. . . . The Seeker's happy smile collapsed as his mind became confused by a conflict of ideas. Did not pride go before the fall which made for unhappiness? A blare of martial music distracted his attention. He never did resolve his conflict.

He noticed some poor, ragged children eagerly and happily watching the parade. These contrasted with some well-dressed rich children who appeared miserably unhappy despite having their every wish granted.

"Why is this so?" he later asked one who should know of such things.

"Well," answered this wise man, "the poor have nothing, and in accepting the worst, they have everything to gain and nothing to lose. Every gain increases their happiness. The rich who have everything have everything to lose and nothing to gain. Every loss increases their unhappiness.

"The poor who suffer a great pain do not feel their many minor pains. Only greater pain is felt. The rich who pay wealth to avoid pain feel their many minor pains and are unhappy.

"The rich, with senses dulled by pastry, cannot enjoy the pleasure of bread. The poor are happy to eat stale bread, happier to eat fresh bread, and ecstatic in eating pastry if they can get it.

"The rich child with his excess toys is not made happier by another one. The poor child without toys finds pleasure in making his own.

"The rich who have all pleasures in youth cannot find greater pleasure as men. The poor who have few pleasures in youth can spend their lives happily seeking what they never enjoyed.

"If the rich have ten million dollars and lose one million, they are unhappy. Suffering comes hard to those who have not suffered. If the poor have ten cents and lose one cent, they too are unhappy, but they are used to suffering, and one more sore on a body covered with sores doesn't make too much difference."

The Seeker of Happiness was enlightened by this discourse. So many secrets of happiness were expressed that he did not know how to unify them into one concise principle. He tried but could not avoid a conclusion that was paradoxical: The poor seek material wealth to be happy, but material wealth destroys happiness. The Seeker did not like this truth and shut it out of his mind. He still planned to find happiness in riches.

The Seeker of Happiness survived his visit to the city. He even grew as his self-disciplined efforts overcame hardship to enable success. In the leisure that followed he had time to contemplate, envy, and covet his neighbors, the Jones family. "If I had a nice home like the Joneses," he said, "I would be happy."

When he got such a home, Neighbor Jones said to his ambitious wife, "We must show our neighbor that we are better than he."

Jones improved his home and the Seeker kept right up with him. This cumulated until the pressures of keeping up with the Joneses made the Seeker of Happiness very unhappy.

"Why should I envy and covet what Jones has," said the Seeker. "While I envy and covet him I am always poor no matter how rich I am. Self-satisfaction can make me happier."

But the Seeker soon forgot this lesson in self-satisfaction. "I would be happy," he said, "to earn $100 a week." Thru his labor union he achieved this. But this rate soon dissatisfied him and he sought $125 to make him happy. He got this and was happy with it until he sought $150. This cumulated until he went on strike to get $200 worth of happiness. It was the final blow to the goose that was laying the golden eggs of his happiness. The Seeker's employer, his labor union, and he himself went bankrupt. Once more he was unhappy working elsewhere for $100. But he adjusted to this rate and was happy in comparing it with less fortunate wage earners. By now he had learned not to compare it with those more fortunate.

This experience cost him much, so he was careful to learn this lesson well: The happier one becomes the happier he wants to be until he exhausts the source of his happiness and starts at the bottom again.

The Seeker, attending a double wedding, noticed one bride beaming with happiness while the other looked rather unhappy. "Surely," he thought, "that happy bride will have a happy marriage and the unhappy bride will have an unhappy marriage."

Paradoxically, this was not the case as he found out later. The weeping bride made the laughing wife, for being so unhappy on her wedding day left her much room to gain happiness. Anything after that was an improvement that brought happiness.

The laughing bride became the weeping wife, for being at her peak of happiness on her wedding day, anything after that was worse in comparison and made her unhappy.

This led the Seeker to conclude that one cannot be happy without a balancing degree of unhappiness as a standard of comparison.

The Seeker saw a girl weeping during the wedding. Such unhappiness was strange at such happy festivities. "Why are you so unhappy?" he asked sympathetically.

From behind a wet handkerchief she sobbed her sad story. "Seeing these happy people makes me unhappy. Seeing those brides makes me miserable. Why? Because gossips already call me an old maid. Why don't I marry? Because I seek the ideal man of my dreams. Using my ideal dream man as a standard of comparison I find fault and reasons for not marrying any man I meet. Now you know why I weep. I'm just a frustrated old maid."

The Seeker left the weeper a little weaker. At her age, he felt, it was futile to advise the obvious—to abandon her dreams for reality, if not for complete happiness, then for a degree of it.

At the wedding reception, the drunkest seemed the happiest. Next day this was reversed. The soberest were the happiest and the drunkest were the unhappiest with their miserable hangovers. Apparently, thought the Seeker soberly, the bigger the drunk, the bigger the hangover. Or, the greater the happiness the greater its balancing degree of unhappiness.

The rich foods at the wedding reception made him recall that as a hillbilly he was happy to eat ground corn. In the city he tasted his first fresh bread. This made him extremely happy until he heard that cake tasted better. He was then unhappy until he acquired the happiness of eating cake. He was happy eating cake until he heard there was greater happiness in eating pie. He soon had tasted all and had tasted the best. Having tasted the best, everything else was worse and made him unhappy.

Munching on a sour hors d'oeuvre he dourly concluded that we tend to think of what we lack, not of what we have. "Why did I have to look for cake when I was happy eating bread? Now nothing makes me happy."

That night he attended services for a deceased friend. Behind his sorrowful demeanor in that vale of tears he felt rather happy in comparing himself to the miserable weepers about him. He recalled the gay wedding reception where he had felt miserable in comparison to those expressing so much more happiness. In expecting a good time at the reception, the reality could not meet his expected hopes. Everything turned out worse than expected. He would have been happier if he had not expected a good time. He expected a miserable time at the wake, but when reality was not as bad as his fears, he felt happier.

It is an ill wind that blows no good. The Seeker was unhappy about many aches and pains, about debts, and about neighbor problems. A hurricane blew away much of this unhappiness. The storm broke his arm which made him unconscious of his many minor aches and pains, and thus happier. He lost his house but gained happiness, for he no

longer worried about debts or in keeping up with the Joneses next door. The storm destroyed many houses, but it also
united many homes and neighborhoods. The hurricane's
roar silenced the gossiper's whisper. All was forgotten, forgiven, and happier in the unity and mutual cooperation for
mutual survival.

He was never so happy about calm weather as he was
after that violent storm. When he finally had time to phi-
losophize, this happy truth came out of the storm: Many
minor troubles and unhappiness disappear with a major
trouble and unhappiness.

During the huricane he felt pretty unhappy about his
stormy problems. He had almost choked with self-pity. But
this self-pity decreased as he increased his pity for others
who had suffered more.

The misery created by the hurricane gave truth to the
proverb: Misery loves company. One's toothache is miserable when no one else's aches or pains. But alongside a
broken back, a toothache becomes insignificant. Misery loves
company because in finding worse misery it felt happier.

The Seeker of Happiness sought happiness the rest of
his days. He learned the rules for achieving happiness, yet
he never found it.

There were times when he suffered terribly. There were
times when he prayed to his God for justice and mercy. It
did not seem just for one as good as he to suffer so. It did
not seem right that God would make the wicked happy and
the good unhappy. There were times when he was ready to
disown his God because of his unhappiness. At these times
it seemed that the law of happiness would be revealed to
him and he would be consoled by its truth: Every sorrow
has its balancing degree of happiness. Then he would wail
in the torment of unhappy torture, "When? Oh! When will
I see this happiness?"

Even the worst of his depressions eventually passed in
the constantly changing balancing cycles of his life.

Eventually he learned that happiness depends upon this constant balancing cyclical change between opposing positive-negative limits of excess-deficiency. It was simply a matter of enjoying a good drink without losing self-control by getting drunk.

He experimented with controlling the degree of happiness by self-disciplined efforts to prevent excess-deficiency, and by self-disciplinary fasts and abstinences when the limits of excess were reached.

He learned that self-disciplined moderation is a key to achieving happiness. But he found difficulty in applying this rule under social conditions where excess was the rule. For a while he thought he had solved this problem. He returned to the valley in the mountains, to the hillbilly land of his birth. There he became a hermit, free to apply the rules of happiness without social interference. But the hermit's subjective spiritual and intellectual happiness was gained only by a balancing loss of objective intellectual and sensual happiness—which required social contact. He gained the happiness of communion with God and Nature, but lost the happiness of intellectual discussion and of a tender loved one.

This experience reemphasized to him that ever repeating principle of happiness: There is no happiness without a balancing degree of unhappiness. He also learned that whether one considered himself happy or unhappy was relative to which he was prepared to perceive on this balance of happiness-unhappiness. Also, what he perceived was relative to the perspective of time and space. An unhappy day did not necessarily mean an unhappy year; unhappiness in one's city did not necessarily mean unhappiness in one's country.

Out of all his seeking, the Seeker concluded that happiness cannot be achieved as a goal. It is the achieving, not the achievement that brings happiness. It is like a child who is happy chasing a beautiful butterfly. When he finally catches it, he has nothing left to inspire happiness—no beauty, no goals, no hope, no happy spirit.

He learned that once happiness is achieved it is subject to all the comparing standards and balancing changes that cause its loss and the seeking of a new degree or kind of happiness.

After a life-time of seeking happiness it was paradoxical and anti-climactic that the seeker should believe happiness cannot be found when sought. It seems that in looking for happiness too much is expected to be found, and it never is found. Without achievement there is only unhappy frustration.

But again paradoxically, in not seeking and expecting happiness, it comes in the constant balancing cyclical changes of man and nature—and any change is a source of happiness from its balancing unhappiness.

Asked for the best means of achieving the greatest degree of happiness, the Seeker of Happiness would answer rather mystically: Truest happiness comes in synchronizing the spirit, mind, and body in rhythm with the balancing laws of nature, and in developing one's natural abilities to their maximum to enable the achievement of one's destined goals.

Even on his death bed the Seeker sought happiness. He was asked by his friend, "If happiness is a goal of life, and permanent happiness cannot be found in life, why do we live?"

The wise old Seeker of Happiness smiled happily as if he had finally found happiness. "If I die and you live," he said, "who will be the happier?"

The cryptic question baffled his friend who felt so sad and unhappy to see the Seeker on his death bed. But after a moment of silence he whispered in awe, "God only knows."

So the Seeker of Happiness, who found happiness in seeking happiness which he never really found, discovered his happiest moment in life at death—seeking ultimate happiness beyond earth.

He died with a happy smile on his lips, for the laws of happiness and God had told him the greater his sufferings on earth, the greater would be his balancing happiness when compared with it.

Thus:

Happiness is relative to time, place, individual, circumstance, and degree.

Happiness is a degree of moderation between excess and deficiency—between misery and ecstasy.

Man is both happy and unhappy relative to a standard of comparison.

Happiness cannot be achieved; it can only be sought and compared.

THE MOTHER AND SON

(On the reward-indifference-punishment trinity)

A young mother loved her son sincerely and always did what was best for him—not what she thought was best but what experts, who should know, thought. As a modern and progressive parent she always practiced the latest advice issued by scientific and psychological experts in child care. As this advice was always improving, she would constantly adjust and change her methods to keep up with the times and with the best.

When her son was born, the experts were advising that parents should accentuate the negative and eliminate the positive. Children were born with evil animal instincts and had no mentality to be reasoned with. Like animals, children had to be trained with a whip to obey and behave. Mothers should constantly complain, criticize, and punish their children to make them start or stop their activity. They should never praise or reward them for that would encourage his free activity and result in a loss of parental control. The child should be trained to be morally good, not pleasantly happy.

The good mother practiced this expert advice but the results were not as predicted by the experts. In fear of her punishment her son lost all his spirit and stopped all his mental and physical activity. He would talk to no one, play with no one, and not even leave his house in fear of doing something wrong. He would sit silently in his room, reading a book or just brooding all day. This inactivity was punished by his mother but it only made him more inactive and punished more. Even if he became more active, his mother would not dare praise or reward him; it would encourage his becoming morally evil.

The mother was becoming more depressed and melancholy than her son when she read of the latest scientific experiments, psychological tests, and statistical surveys. These indicated that child care experts now advised mothers to accentuate the positive and eliminate the negative. Children were born pure and good and should be given all opportunity to express this good nature. All one had to do was to understand children and reason with them as with adults. Like cultured flowers they should be handled with tender, loving care to develop the best in them. Mothers should never criticize, complain, or punish their children. Rather, they should constantly praise and reward their good activities and understand their bad activities as being due to poor parental guidance. Mothers should make their children happy, not good, for if they were happy they would be good.

The good mother did this until her son lost all his inhibitions and became an exuberant exhibitionist in his activity. He could do anything and he did everything. He disobeyed his mother, swore at and kicked his father, tortured his pet cat, and wrecked most of the furniture. He did anything to be aggressive and antagonistic, but his mother knew from her learning that he was only releasing his inhibitions to prevent aggression and antagonism. He did nothing which the mother could praise or reward, and she could only ignore his bad acts for any criticism or punishment would be sure to make him neurotically unhappy.

Just about the time the house was ready to break up and the parents were ready to break down over the son, the mother read the latest scientifically proven and psychologically tested method of child care. Now the experts said the child was a natural being who should be left alone to let nature take its course. Mothers should avoid being positive or negative to their children, but should strive to be neutrally indifferent. They should neither praise or reward, nor criticize or punish their children.

The good mother did this to her son but observed that as a result her son began to act strangely. He would suddenly start activity and just as suddenly stop it. He could never seem to make up his mind. As his thinking became confused he began to stumble and jerk in his body and stutter with his speech. He became utterly confused and never seemed to know where to go, what to do, and how to do it.

This went on until the mother, who repressed both her praise and her criticism, outwardly became as unemotional as a statue but emotionally inhibited to the point of explosion. By this time her son had matured enough to give his views of the experiments that now made him feel like a laboratory guinea pig.

"Mother," he said, "criticize or condemn me if you cannot praise or commend me. Until you do one or the other I do not know where to go, what to do, or how to do it. I will stop what is punished, or do what is rewarded, but with neither punishment nor reward, I go nowhere in confusion."

The pitiful mother had recently read the latest theory on child care. The experts now said parents should be negative and scold the child to mold him and to never praise the child to raise him. She took this scientifically proven and psychologically tested advice of the experts and burned it in her garbage disposal incinerator before it could destroy the body, mind, and spirit of other mothers and sons.

Then calling her son to her she put her arms about him tenderly and said, "I will let my conscience, my motherly intuition, and my common sense guide me in your care. When you are good, I will let my rewarding praise elate you and inspire your activity. But if you are bad, my son, I will let my punishing criticism deflate you and repress your activity. And if I am confused and do not know whether to reward or punish you, I will let you be the judge of what I should do."

The unhappy boy turned his sad eyes up to his mother's but now they seemed to sparkle happily thru the tear drop that trickled down. Then his confused look seemed to be replaced by one of self-disciplined self-control. He hugged his mother long, tenderly, and gratefully. For the first time he seemed to know where he stood in relation to his mother, his parents, and his home. He now had someone, his mother, to enlighten his ignorance and to give him guiding standards, values, and principles. He had someone to let him know where to go, what to do and how to do it—by rewarding and punishing him when he deserved it.

Thus:

Punishment makes the inhibited introvert; reward makes the exhibiting extrovert; moderation makes the average ambivert.

Reward expresses; punishment represses; indifference distresses.

Achievement elates; frustration deflates; conflict confuses.

THE PROGRESSIVE SPORTSMEN

(On the balance of nature)

On a large, lush island a group of progressive sportsmen organized a committee to decrease fish and game destruction, increase its production, and improve fishing and hunting conditions. After a thorough investigation the committee chairman reported: "We find that otters are killing fishes; wolves are killing deer; woodpeckers warn game of approaching hunters, and swamps close many areas to duck hunters. To improve fishing and hunting conditions the committee recommends the elimination of these problems."

The progressive sportsmen voted for an immediate campaign to eliminate these conditions on their island. Otters were trapped and exterminated. A bounty was placed on wolves and succeeded in eliminating them. Shotguns made woodpeckers extinct. Swamps and marshes were drained. Who could deny the bountiful benefits of such a progressive program?

The sportsmen eagerly awaited the opening of the fishing and hunting season to reap the rewards of their praiseworthy efforts. But the momentous day was dark and dreary for reasons other than the weather. The expectant sportsmen were dumbfounded to find not more fish and game, but less. They did have more room to hunt in reclaimed swamps and were not bothered by woodpeckers, but there were no ducks in the reclaimed swamps and no game to be warned by woodpeckers.

In panicky alarm the cry rang thru field and forest,

"What happened?" From valley to mountain top was heard the anguished wail, "What happened?" So another committee was organized to find out what happened. After intensive investigation it reported: "We find that otters killed only diseased fish which were too slow to escape them. By eliminating otters the diseased fish cumulated and infected healthy fish which cumulated to an epidemic. Now there are no fish left."

A frustrated fisherman whined an excuse, "But nobody told us this would happen. Maybe we should bring otters back."

This brought no response from the dejected and numb assembly so the chairman continued his report. "After we killed the wolves which were killing deer, the deer cumulated to such an excess that the rangeland grass could not support them all. Half of them starved to death that winter and the other half the next winter. Now there are no deer left."

An unhappy hunter interrupted and moaned, "Oy! What did we do? Let's get some wolves back right away."

The chairman ignored this interruption and continued. "When we drained swamps and marshes to make more room available to hunt ducks it was wasted effort. The ducks failed to make their annual return, for they had no water to return to."

A duck hunter let out a long wail like a sick duck, buried his head in his hands, and said no more.

The cold and indifferent chairman went on with the ugly truth and consequences: "When we exterminated woodpeckers which feasted on tree-boring insects, the insects multiplied and feasted on trees. The trees weakened, lost their resistance, and were all killed in a blight. In wiping out woodpeckers we wiped out a forest with all its birds and animals. In other words, gentlemen, we have destroyed ourselves as hunters and fishermen, for there is nothing left to hunt and fish."

The conclusion of this report brought a conglomeration of moaning and groaning, cussing and blustering, weeping and griefing, damning and slamming. Order was finally restored out of chaos and another committee was organized. It was to find ways and means of getting fish and game back. If possible, it was to return to the conditions that existed before the progressive campaign to advance their sport. The radical and progressive sportsmen had become reactionary and regressive.

But the wheels of progress, prodded by the progressive sportsmen, progressed without losing momentum. Without fish the lakes and ponds became slimy with decay as pests breeded and pestilence spread its deadly misery over the island.

The rangeland, without roots to hold rain or hold soil together, had its top soil eroded away by rain. Because no blades of grass protected the top soil from the wind, the skies became black with dust storms. Rangeland turned to desert land and grassy slopes to sand dunes.

Without swamps as natural reservoirs, excess rains became ravaging floods that uprooted trees and topsoil and left fish high, dry, and dead. Drought followed flood, for without natural swamp reservoirs to release reserve water, underground water tables lowered. Springs, rivers, lakes, and wells dried up as the water table went down. Without water, vegetation withered and died. Without water and vegetation, birds and animals died.

This drainage effected not only inland conditions but also the ocean waters surrounding the island. When tidal marshes were drained with the swamps to make more room available to hunt and fish, the hunters found that they not only lost all sports hunting and fishing but all commercial fishing as well. Without tidal marshes the fish, lobsters, crabs, and oysters of the ocean lost their main breeding grounds and main source of food.

Without trees, rain water could not be absorbed and

stored to prevent flood and drought; top soil could not be held together to prevent wind and rain erosion; winds could not be slowed down to prevent wind damage and dust storms; the hot sun could not be absorbed to make cool days nor could this heat be released to make cold nights warm; birds and animals could find no protection. All vegetation withered or washed away. All became desolate and deserted desert. Nothing could survive, whether fish, animal, bird, or man; they either died or moved away to greener pastures to fight others in the competition for survival.

When nothing was left to destroy on the island, nature continued its progress. A blade of grass became two, then many. This enabled a tree to root and be followed by other trees. These stored rain water which trickled to a brook, to a stream, then to a river. Fish, animals, and birds mysteriously appeared from nowhere to inhabit the new forest. Destruction had changed to construction in the balancing cycles of nature.

What? What happened to the last sportsmen's committee? Well, they were working too hard and worrying so much that they all decided to quit and go fishing. Thus:

There is no change in nature without balancing changes

Everything plays its part to maintain the Balance of Nature.

Violent readjustment is the penalty for upsetting the Balance of Nature.

THE UNHAPPY RICH MAN

(On self-disciplined moderation)

A certain man was considered to be the world's wealthiest. He was rich enough to buy anything. But he was an unhappy rich man. So one day he made up his mind to buy some happiness.

When hungry he ate what he desired. When thirsty he drank what he desired. When curious he saw and heard what he desired. At the least sign of pain or illness an army of doctors and nurses soothed him with sweet medicine, with gentle massages, and with soothing sympathy. He never did physical work so he spent much time in boring idleness or asleep in bed. Violent storms of nature and of man were not allowed to disturb him. His vast wealth bought him anything his craving senses desired. But the more he strove to buy his happiness the more unhappy he became. His senses became senseless, his mind became witless, and his spirit became lifeless. His eyes dulled, his smile sneered, and his body drooped in dejection. He was most unhappy with all the things that common people envied as the only means to happiness.

Dozens of handshaking, grinning, optimistic, joke-telling experts on happiness became rich in teaching him how to be happy. These phony, frivolous philosophers of friendship fooled him. They only made him more conscious of his unhappiness and thus more unhappy.

His unhappiness became most bitter upon seeing a crippled beggar in rags selling apples on a cold street corner. The beggar was smiling, bright-eyed, active and gay—he was happy. The rich man invited the poor man to his home. There the beggar proved to be a learned man who was well versed in that wisdom which brings in no money. He was wise in the knowledge of great thoughts of great thinkers from all ages and places. He was a poor man materially, but he was a rich man intellectually, and a happy man spiritually. He needed little money, for he had no need to buy happiness.

The rich foolish man asked the poor wise man, "Why are you so happy with nothing to make you happy, and why am I so unhappy with everything to make me happy?" The wise man replied, "Can a rich man enjoy the happiness that a starving man has over a stale crust of bread? Can the rich enjoy the happiness of drinking cool water as enjoyed by one lost in the desert? Can the rich be made happy by nature's beauties as is the poor who have no luxuries to distract these beauties? Do the rich suffer the pain and illness of the poor which brings the happiness of relief known only to those who suffer? Can the idle rich appreciate the happy relaxation that follows hard work? Can the sheltered rich feel the happy calm that follows storm or the happy peace that follows violence?"

The rich man's eyes began to glow and his face began to beam as the light of this wisdom radiated from his understanding mind. The poor wise man continued, "The poor learn to be content with little sufferings and so they require a greater suffering to feel unhappy. But the unsuffering rich require only a little suffering to feel very unhappy. The suffering poor need only a little relief to feel much happiness, while the rich need much relief to feel a little happier."

The unhappy rich man heeded this advice and offered the wise pauper rich rewards for his wisdom. But the wise man practiced what he preached. He accepted only a book from the rich man's library.

Following the wise man's wisdom, the rich man renounced his goal of buying happiness. He began to seek happiness by self-disciplined efforts to be moderate in all things. By suffering the hunger of fasts and abstinences, and the discomforts of long trips into the wilderness, the rich man began to appreciate the happiness of sensory pleasures. By dismissing his servants and doing creative physical labor he began to enjoy the intellectual elation of solving problems while gaining the physical well-being of a healthy body. By personally giving to the poor and needy he began to feel the greatest of happiness—the spiritual happiness which comes only thru the soul. Then as the old stories say, he lived happily ever after—because he suffered ever after.

Thus:

Without sadness there is no happiness.

True happiness is a balance between spiritual, intellectual, and sensual pleasures.

Having nothing, every gain brings happiness; having all, every loss brings unhappiness.

THE SCIENTIST

(On balancing the trinity of perspective)

A metaphysicist, a logician, and a scientist were assigned a task of jointly solving a problem. The metaphysicist wanted a solution based on intuitive insight. The logician thought he could get a better solution by logical deduc- tions. But the scientist wanted experiments to formulate a conclusion.

The scientist said, "This is a scientific age. Science has proven the ridiculousness of mystic mumbo-jumbo and the fallacy in logical linguistics."

The scientist was then asked, "But how do you know that your scientific conclusions are truth?"

And the scientist replied, "I see, therefore I know. Truth is only what is perceived thru the senses. I do not dabble in the deceptive tricks of mental logic or the superstition of mystic metaphysics."

The logician reasoned on this remark and concluded, "Then you know that there is nothing beyond the horizon for you can see nothing beyond it."

The scientist replied, "I have been beyond the horizon and I have seen; therefore, I know what is beyond it."

The logician reasoned again, "What you once saw be- yond the horizon may not be there now; therefore, to be- lieve something is there because it was once there is a metaphysical belief, or a logical mental deduction, not a scientific sensory truth."

"At least it was seen," observed the scientist. "It is not like the fantasies of metaphysics which derive so-called truths from what can never be seen thru the senses."

The metaphysician contemplated this and declared, "Then you know that nothing is beyond earth in the black spaces of the night sky, for no one has been out there to see."

The scientist answered, "I have seen beyond earth with a telescope; I have seen; therefore, I know."

The metaphysician added, "You cannot see beyond your telescope's range, so you will deny that something is there for you cannot see it. And if that is so, why do you waste time, effort, and money building bigger telescopes? If you believe something is beyond what you cannot see with your present telescope then your truth is a metaphysical revealed truth, not a scientific sensory truth."

The scientist defended himself, "You misunderstand what true science is. Of course the scientist believes— Oops! I do not want to use this unscientific word, but how can I avoid it. Anyway, the scientist believes that the balanced and progressive order of nature extends in a structural pattern beyond the known. Therefore, we can know the truth of the unknown before we can see it."

The metaphysician jumped in and said, "But that is what I have always believed in and stated. It is what has been revealed to me by metaphysical revelation which grasps insight into what cannot be sighted by any senses."

The logician also snapped in with, "And that is what I have always reasoned to be true and so stated. I have concluded this as a result of logical inductions and deductions which enable my mind to conceive of truth."

The scientist began to be unscientifically emotional. "I cannot agree with you metaphysicians and logicians for you both fail to apply scientific methods in making your over-generalized statements."

"Well, now!" said the metaphysician and the logician at the same time, "What scientific method did you use to make that over-generalized statement?"

Meanwhile, their employer who was seeking a joint solution to his problem stepped into the picture and said, "Well, at least you all agree that you all make general statements. Now can you all agree on a common general solution to my problem?"

Thus:

Knowledge thru the senses is limited.

Beyond material physics is mental logic and beyond this is spiritual metaphysics.

The spiritualist conceives thru the soul's revelation; the intellectual perceives thru mental logic; the materialist sees thru sensory feeling.

THE FREEDOM FIGHTERS

(On the balancing trinity of freedom)

The radical, young, idealistic student was emotionally fanatical in his verbal fight for freedom. He could not comprehend the calm moderation of the wise old philosopher regarding those who fought for freedom. Gesticulating freely the student argued, "The Medieval man of faith wanted freedom of spiritual expression and freedom to worship as he pleased. As a chivalrous knight he fought religious crusades for his church against the Saracen infidel. He knew freedom was worth fighting and dying for."

"Maybe so," interrupted the professor in a pacifying tone, "but while fighting for spiritual freedom did he not, in following blind faith, sacrifice his freedom of intellectual expression? Did he not, in following the chivalric code to inhibit sensual pleasure, sacrifice his sensual freedom? I believe Medieval man's freedom was negative in value. It was expressed in the doctrine of the 'Ten Commandments' and the dictates of the conscience which say, 'Thou shalt not do this—but are free to do anything else.'"

The student would not permit this answer to silence his free expression. "The Renaissance man of reason," he said, "wanted freedom of intellectual expression and freedom to live by his own cultural customs and traditions. As a gallant cavalier he fought patriotic wars for his Fatherland against enemy nations. He must have known freedom was worth fighting and dying for."

"Maybe so," interjected the wise old man in a moderating tone, "but while fighting for intellectual freedom did he not, in thinking contrary to his religious faith, forfeit his spiritual freedom? Did he not, in letting reason moderate his sensual pleasure, forfeit his sensual freedom? I think Renaissance man's freedom was neutral in value. It was based on the philosophy of the 'Social Contract' and free-will which said, 'You may do this—but let rational, self-disciplined moderation be your guide.'"

"Well, anyway," said the frustrated and dejected fighter for freedom, "modern man with his sense of reality seeks freedom of physical expression and democratic freedom to do as he pleases. As a cynical realist he fights economic wars against authoritarian dictatorships to maintain his ma-terial benefits and his cultural pleasures and happiness Isn't his freedom and happiness worth fighting and dying for?"

"Maybe so," answered the old professor in a concilia-tory tone, "but while fighting for physical and material freedom did he not relinquish his spiritual freedom to prac-tice moral values? Did he not, in striving for sensual pleas-ures, relinquish his intellectual freedom to practice self-disciplined moderation? I see Modern man's freedom as being positive in value. It is expressed in the constitutional 'Bill of Rights' which says, 'You are free to do this—but not anything else if so dictated.'"

The flabbergasted fighter for freedom shouted back in alarm, "Are you implying that all these men were foolish in fighting for freedom?"

He was ready to report the subversive attitude of this authoritarian professor to the dean. Such unlicensed free-dom of expression should not be permitted.

"No," said the wise old professor soothingly to calm stormy waters, "but these freedom fighters fought for only one-third of their freedom. They had to sacrifice two-thirds of their freedom to gain it."

"Then you think it is futile to fight for freedom," said the disillusioned-looking freedom fighter.

"No," replied the scholar, "these freedom fighters rightfully fought for a freedom they did not have. But in gaining the freedom they wanted, in balance, they lost a freedom they wanted less."

"Then it was worthwhile fighting and dying for a freedom they did not have," beamed the elated student at having the professor agree with him.

"Maybe so," replied the professor, "I myself have never fought for freedom; maybe that is why I lack the spiritual freedom of Medieval man, the intellectual freedom of Renaissance man, and the sensual freedom of Modern man. But I do have a little of each kind of freedom, not just one of them. I have, I think, a balanced degree of spiritual, intellectual, and sensual freedom, even tho I can apply only one of these freedoms at a time, and can do so as occasion demands. Now my young fighter for freedom, which do you think is the greater freedom—to have much of one, or a little of all three?"

Ending his question he slowly walked away, leaving the dumbfounded student agape at the question still hanging over his head.

Thus:

In balance, as one freedom is gained others are lost.

Man can have spiritual, intellectual, or sensual freedom, but only one at a time.

Man is free to decide whether his freedom shall be spiritual, intellectual, or sensual.

THE CHICKEN AND THE EGG

(On the balancing trinity of truth)

Down on the farm behind a haystack, two hired hands sat contentedly. Their supervisor was away so now they could relax and play. Watching clouds slowly passing by and nonchalantly chewing long straws, they drifted into a slow and easy argument.

"You know, Hiram," said one to the other, "I think that chickens came first and caused the egg."

Hiram switched his straw to the other corner of his mouth and drawled, "I don't know about that, Zeke, I think the egg came first and caused the chicken."

They both paused in silence, shook their heads slowly— one nodding yes and the other nodding no. Then both drew upon their straws to further chew on this barnyard philosophy.

Their deep meditation was suddenly shattered by an unpleasant but familiar voice. They did not see the speaker but their reason told them it was their supervisor.

"You are both right," said the voice from nowhere, "and maybe you are both wrong. Maybe the chicken and the egg caused each other. Apparently neither of you perceives the original cause which can neither be reasoned nor seen but must be believed."

Th guilt stricken workers looked at each other with the blank faces of blank minds whose understanding is blank.

The unseen speaker, not seeing all this blankness, continued. "You are like two men who look at a see-saw and debate which way it moves. One says, 'It is moving up.' The other says, 'No, it is moving down.' Do not both speak the truth in what they see even tho they have contrary views? Each sees only a part of the whole truth. They may both get a third view, a mental view, and reason that the see-saw is going up and down at the same time. But there is a fourth view which they do not see. Between the up-and-down movement is a point of no movement. This point cannot be seen or reasoned but must be believed if the whole truth is to be understood. Likewise, my lazy chicken eggheads, between the chicken and the egg is a truth which cannot be seen or reasoned but can only be believed."

Looking around frantically, Hiram and Zeke saw their supervisor coming around the haystack. He too had been resting contentedly behind the haystack before being interrupted by the intruders.

The supervisor looked at them sternly and said, "You could not see me, but you reasoned it was I by my voice. Now you may not see or reason this, but believe me," he said to the pop-eyed, open-mouthed shirkers, "get back to work before I make scrambled eggs out of you!"

It may be unbelievable and unreasonable, but smoke could be seen coming from their heels as they ran back to work.

Thus:

Some truths can only be believed, only reasoned, or only seen.

Parts of the whole truth may have to be believed, reasoned, and seen.

Truth is a trinity of negative, neutral, and positive values.

THE DYING PATIENT

(On the balancing human trinity)

A dying patient was visited by a staff of doctors for diagnosis. The medical doctor, after probing here and there and everywhere, said authoritatively, "After analyzing the patient's body, my opinion is that his symptoms derive from physical conditions."

The psychologist, after testing reactions here and there and everywhere, concluded expertly, "I analyzed the patient's mind and my opinion is that his symptoms derive from mental conditions."

The psychiatrist, after questioning here, probing there, and testing everywhere, said without hesitation, "After analyzing the patient's body and mind, I would say that according to the latest theories the symptoms are either mental or physical, or they are both, or maybe neither."

A priest who was standing by to administer last rites to the dying patient was not on the medical staff but felt it his duty to say something. "I do not wish to impose on your professional integrity," he said, "by giving you my opinion, but I feel it is my duty as spiritual adviser to say that the patient is more than just a body and a mind. He is also a spiritual being. I believe the patient is dying because he has lost his will to live. He has lost his spirit. He can no more live without a spiritual soul than he can live without a physical heart or an intellectual mind."

A mortician interrupted at this moment to say bluntly, "While you all debated the patient died. But let me say that in my analysis of bodies I have yet to find a body operating without a mind or a mind operating without a body. As for this spiritual thing; well, that's out of my line unless you're talking about something to drink."

Thus:

The human being is a balanced trinity of spiritual, intellectual, and physical beings.

Body affects mind; mind affects body; spirit affects both.

The eye specialist blinds himself to all but the eye when he looks into the eye.

ID, EGO, AND SUPEREGO

(On the balancing trinity of goals)

Three psychiatrists attended a convention and as to be expected at such affairs, the three experts disagreed on a common problem. Their problem was to find the basis of man's spiritual, mental, and physical activity.

Doctor Idduerf of the sexual school of psychiatry said, "Sexual desires and sensory pleasures are the basis of man's physical and mental activity. Understanding man's subconscious physical and sensory sexual desires, his past sexual inhibitions, and then releasing and resolving these will prevent and cure his diseased brain."

Doctor Adlerego of the power school of psychiatry said, "No, the drive for achievement and power is the basis of man's physical and mental activity. Understanding man's conscious and subconscious emotional rationalizations, his past and present inferiority complexes, and his compensating power drives, and then redirecting them in another direction will prevent and cure man's mental and physical ailments."

Young Doctor Superego, leader of the security school of psychiatry said, "No, the striving for security is the basis of man's spiritual, mental, and physical activity. Understanding man's symbolic heritage from the past, as they effect his present moral standards and intuitive revelations, his present and future views regarding his individual and social security, and restoring his faith and hope by achievement, will prevent and cure man's spiritual, mental, and physical problems."

Mr. Detinu was not a psychiatrist for he held no college degree, but had spent his entire life on psychiatric problems. He was given the floor after making a nuisance of himself by trying to get attention. He said, "You all apparently speak profound truths, but paradoxically you all disagree on the same problem. In effect your disagreements accuse each other of being untrue. Maybe the greater truth can be found in a common agreement. We all agree that sex, power, and security are basic goals to be achieved. Can we all agree that the common denominator here, goals, are the basis of man's spiritual, mental, and physical activity?"

When they all seemed to nod in agreement to this, the layman was encouraged to go on. "Maybe the agreeable whole truth is composed of disagreeable part-truths. Maybe sex determines much of man's physical activity, and power his mental activity, and security and symbolic inheritance his spiritual activity. Can the greater truth be that the individual is a triad personality—a trinity? Is he not only a physical being, but also a mental being and a spiritual being? Can it be that each of you specializes in only one of these beings which happens to express itself more than the others in the individual?"

The three psychiatrists would not deny that each spoke the truth, yet they did seem to contradict each other by their disagreements. So they accepted the greater truth as stated by the layman: Each spoke the truth only in terms of one part of the human trinity.

They accepted this truth silently, for they feared expressing publicly what was not professionally acceptable or popular. But their spokesman did his duty to protect their professional status. He roared out, "We cannot accept such radical, unproven theories, for you lack the proper degrees and experience to qualify you as a psychiatric authority.

Now will the Master-at-arms please escort the uninvited person to the door so that we may continue our efforts to seek and find common answers to our problems."
Thus:

Goals are the basis of man's spiritual, mental, and physical activity.

Security, pleasure, and achievement are basic goals.

Truth is a trinity of negative, neutral, and positive values.

THE INSTIGATING INTEGRATOR

(On the balancing trinity of man and unified principles)

Three of the most learned scholars in the land attended a conference which was to clarify the meaning, purposes, and goals of life and man. Man, it was assumed, had to have these as a reason for being, and as a reason for stimulating and integrating his spiritual, mental, and physical activity.

The solemn and revered priest from the Gothic cathedral preached this doctrine: "I believe man has a mystical, religious soul which strives for spiritual and ideational goals."

The serious and honored philosopher from the classic university taught this thesis: "I think man has a rational, philosophical mind which strives for intellectual and idealistic goals."

The interesting and famous scientist from the functional laboratory made this hypothesis: "I see man as being an experimenting body which strives for sensual and realistic goals."

The moderator, apparently confused by this disagreement, interjected, "How can this be? You are the foremost authorities in your fields of knowledge, yet you all disagree as to the nature of man and his goals."

The priest, philosopher, and scientist hemmed, hawed, and frowned, but came up with no answer. They stroked their chins in deep meditation, disputation, and consultation, but still came up with no answer to resolve their disagreement. They all did agree in saying, "Obviously, what I have said is the one and only truth."

As the stalemate stagnated to a standstill a young student attending the conference stood up and said with manifest humility, "With all due respect may I give my personal views on this three-way controversy to make a synthesis of your thesis and antithesis?"

The moderator and the three specialized wisemen were dumbfounded and flabbergasted by the audacity of the youth. Before they could collect their collective wits the youth continued: "You all say you speak the ultimate truth regarding the nature and goals of man. One of you says man is spiritual, another says he is intellectual, and the third says he is sensual. If all of you speak the truth, then it is logical to conclude that man is all three combined or integrated into one—he is spiritual, intellectual, and sensual at the same time."

The priest meditated; the philosopher disputated, and the scientist agitated as they all nodded in silent agreement to the youth.

Agreement inspired the youth to go on. "But how can this be? If man is a spiritual mystic who gains knowledge intuitively, what happens to the intellectual part of him which cannot logically prove this intuition? What happens to the sensual part of him which cannot sensually verify either the intuition or the logic? Yet each of you claims man has only one particular nature. If man has only one nature, then one of you speaks truth and the other two speak falsely."

The three experts pointed forefingers at their chests, shook their heads negatively, and looked wildly at each other as if to say, "Not me!"

Without waiting for their denying heads to stop wagging the eager youth went on, "If you all speak the truth, then can it be that man has three natures but can express only one of these natures at a time?"

The priest was suddenly struck by a flash of intuition, the philosopher by a logical deduction, and the scientist by suddenly seeing the boy clearly thru his thick bi-focals. Their agreement was unanimous; the student was out of order.

"Who let that little boy in!" uttered the priest.

"What right does he have to tell us what to think!" exclaimed the philosopher.

"Who gave him authority to speak!" cried the scientist.

So the moderator had the instigating integrator expelled from the consternated conference.

The conference went on without argument or debate for no one would disagree with the experts who united in agreement to disprove the insolent student who had such contempt for their authority. They all finally came to an agreement: Man is a mystical, logical experimenter.

The words of these major experts were published thru out the land. Minor experts wrote books on their words; sub-experts wrote books on the experts' books, and laymen, who never read the original words, wrote books on the sub-experts' books.

Millions of students read these books and from then on lost sleep, acquired headaches, and had their minds go blank in a mental block that could not intuitively reveal, logically deduce, or experimentally see how man can be at one and the same time a mystical, philosophical scientist.

Meanwhile, the youthful instigating integrator of knowledge, the would-be synthesizer and unifier of opposites, became a forgotten chemist who spent the rest of his days neutralizing and synthesizing acids and alkalines to salts, and changing salts back to acids and alkalines. He no longer mentioned the synthesis of negative, neutral, and positive values for he could find no one who would listen to him. It was obvious to all that his strange ideas were contrary to all authority—and might did make right in the weird world of reality.

Thus:

Man is not a dual personality; he is a triple personality.

Man cannot be a mystic, a philosopher, and a scientist at one and the same time.

Man is a spiritual, intellectual, and sensual being, but expresses only one of these at a time—like a true hypocrite.

THE ONE WOMAN WHO WAS THREE

(On the balancing trinity of man and unified principles)

Three renowned artists entered a contest to determine which could best portray the true nature of woman. Their model was the same woman. This woman was without benefit of makeup as she posed in a bare, unfurnished room. Each artist saw the same woman with his physical eye but each portrayed what he saw in his mind's eye.

The first artist, who was of an idealistic nature, portrayed a radiant, innocent-looking madonna. Her heavenly, sad face radiated within a shining halo. She was tenderly nesting a helpless child in her arms. This saintly looking mother was dressed in a neat, modest, unadorned robe. A stained glass church window made up the background of the portrait. The portrait was entitled: Unachieved Spiritual Love's Eternal Hope.

The second artist, who was of an idyllic nature, portrayed a beautiful, intelligent-looking young lady. Her enigmatic, smiling face was softly powdered and painted. She was soothingly caressing a pet dog on her lap. This natural looking mistress was dressed in a rich, ornate, bejeweled gown. A classically designed tapestry of nature made up her background. The portrait was entitled: Expectant Romantic Love's Youthful Pleasure.

The third artist, who was of a realistic nature, portrayed an ugly, stupid-looking hag. Her obscene face was scarred and wrinkled. She was cruelly clutching a scrawny cat in her hands. This satanic looking witch was dressed in garish, dirty, tattered rags. Empty bottles, rat traps, and crumbling plaster walls made up her background. The portrait was entitled: Achieved Love's Cynical Frustration.

The judges of the contest made their decision: All three artists equally won a share of the prize for all had equally shared in depicting the true nature of woman. Each artist had depicted a separate nature of woman. These separate pictures combined to make the whole unified picture of her. The three pictures unified, depicted universal and eternal woman as she constantly changes in the eyes of individual man in the cycle of his life, and in the eyes of general man in the cycle of his civilization.

Upon hearing this decision, a woman spectator, obviously resentful, was heard to say, "Of course, if three women artists painted the same man they would also portray him in a similar manner. They would portray a man, not only as a holy saint and a romantic lover, but also as an ugly beast." Thus:

Truth is a unity of diversity.

When civilized women change from madonnas to mistresses to monsters, men change to monks.

The lover sees a halo where the rejected suitor sees blemishes.

THE ODD CHARACTER

(On unified principles)

During the evening college coffee break my scholarly friend asked, "Who is that odd character who argues so dogmatically?"

Apologetically I replied, "Oh, him! He's just an odd character who's frustrated because he can't publish his manuscript. He's trying to tell the world orally what he can't do in print. But, as you can see, the more he tries to impress others, the more unimpressed they become. I haven't seen him convince anyone yet. Anyway, don't let him bother you. When he realizes his words fall on deaf ears, he goes out of his way to avoid mentioning his system."

My puzzled-looking friend put down his coffee and exclaimed, "System? What do you mean, system?"

"Oh, his book is about a system of key words—'unified principle key words' I think he calls them. This system is supposed to condense facts into principles and these principles into about twenty unified principles which are symbolized by key words. All he talks about are his key words. They include such words as cycle, balance, goal, progressive range, negative, neutral, positive, and what-have-you. These are supposed to be means to finding ultimate truths and the sources of knowledge. Anyway, he seems to think he's a philosopher, in fact, a philosopher's philosopher. He claims to have synthesized all other philosophies into the one and ultimate philosophy. What an imagination! I never could understand what he was talking about—sure sounds crazy to me."

"Yes, and he sure looks it!" agreed my friend blowing across the top of his cooled coffee.

Pointing to the argumentative character I continued, "You haven't heard anything yet. He claims educational foundations spend millions to find what he has already. Personally, I think these foundations are as fantastic as his system. Look at the way he acts! Does he look like a superman? Yet he's got a nerve to think his system can change the conscious and subconscious mind of man to make him a superman or something. He was telling me last week that his key words can affect civilized man as much as the alphabet affected uncivilized man. His unified principle key words are supposed to synthesize ideas like the letters of the alphabet synthesize sounds. Who am I to argue with him!"

My friend answered confusedly, "He's a sort of semanticist then, isn't he?"

"I don't know what you'd call him besides a nitwit. But he doesn't think so. He thinks he's wiser than Solomon—and only he knows all the answers. He think he's qualified to teach any subject. It seems that his unified principles apply to all fields of knowledge, whether theological, political, social, psychological, economical, or cultural. He thinks, I don't know how, that principles that apply to the individual also apply to the family, group, city, nation, and civilization. But why argue with him; everything he says is an all-inclusive generality which you can't prove or disprove."

The face of my friend twitched as he blurted out, "He must be a psycho! Anyone who thinks like that must be compensating for something."

I avoided my friend's anxious eyes as I answered, "Yes, he probably has an inferiority complex or something. But the paradox is that he is also a conceited egotist—loves to see his name in print. Maybe you've seen his weekly letter to the editor of the local newspaper? They're all about the decline of this civilization. We're supposed to be approaching a dark age unless we return to something called spiritual self-disciplined character and values. Man! What a pessimistic prophet of doom! According to him, we've been declining ever since the Renaissance. That's supposed to be the peak of our civilization. He claims to prove this by the negative values existing before that time, the neutral values at that time, and the positive values since then. What he means by this is Greek to me. Anyway, according to him, as we decline another civilization is supposed to be rising. How far-fetched can you be! Anybody knows this is ridiculous!"

My friend burst out, "Holy cow! Is that guy really serious!"

"He is," I informed him, "and wait 'til you hear him talk about his cycles and balances of history. It'll drive you crazy as he is. And get this! He's not only a philosopher's philosopher but a historian's historian. He has a philosophy of history, or so he claims, which is a synthesis of Toynbee, Spencer, Gibbons, and any other philosoper of history you can mention."

My friend raised his eyebrows superciliously, "At his age! Why, he's still an undergraduate!"

"That's right," I informed him, "in fact he says the same thing about any scholar you can think of. He says his work unifies all knowledge whether theological, philosophical, or scientific. He can say what he wants, but his biased frame of reference can rationalize any fact into his so-called system. If he can't rationalize it in words he'll do it in pictures. He's always trying to force every fact he hears into six simple drawings. These are supposed to symbolize his unified principles to explain all knowledge."

My friend laughed and in ridicule exclaimed, "It must

be some system if he has to use mumbo-jumbo, abraca-dabra, and mystic signs and symbols to impress the ignorant and superstitious!"

I didn't think him very funny and said seriously, "It's not such a ridiculous idea as you may think. Don't forget that the letters of the alphabet are symbolic pictures to communicate what cannot otherwise be expressed. And that isn't all; his system is supposed to be the basis of creative ideas. Maybe it is, for he comes up with hundreds of crazy ideas, even if they don't make sense—well, at least most of them don't. And so it goes. I could tell you about hundreds of his fantastic ideas. But why go on, you'll hear from him soon enough. And if you really want to be bothered, just give him a little encouragement. Man! Will he pester you! His dogmatic statements and tricky ques-tions will irritate you to where you're ready to throw rocks at him."

My friend laughed heartily and then spoke with au-thority, "Well, I suppose he has had nothing to do except to have someone support him in his ivory dream tower. When he gets out of school the facts of life will change his radical ideas."

I didn't want to but I had to disagree, "Maybe so," I said, "but he should have gotten some reality from the slums he was born into and from his six years as a war-time naval electrician. I've also heard that he's been a pick-and-shovel laborer, a factory worker, and a legal investigator. He also is married and has two kids. So you figure it out; the real side of his life doesn't go along with his unreal ideas. Frankly, he's been around a lot more than I have. Maybe his experiences did teach him something that I don't know about."

With a wishful gleam in his eye my friend said, "Maybe he's got a split personality of a what do you call it —Oh, yes, a schizophrenic!"

"Who knows," I went on, "personally, I don't think he

knows what in hell he's talking about—but then, maybe he does."

"I would think," thought my talkative friend who was beginning to irritate me, "that if he had anything at all to say he would use it to get his own ideas across."

"Well," I replied almost defensively, "tell him that and he'll come back with one of his ever-ready generalities. He'll say he's a product of his age, not of his ideas. I think he really believes that if he'd been brought up on his own ideas he'd make Plato look like a moron compared to his genius."

"That's a hypocrite for you!" preached my over-generalizing friend. " 'Don't do as I do; do as I say.' "

"So what can you do!" I spouted in a manner to put my pompous friend in his place. "It would be a dull place for all of us without neurotic characters like him."

"I suppose so," agreed my unfazed friend, "Look! The students arguing with him are leaving—and do they sound mad! What sarcastic names they're calling him!"

"Don't let it bother you," I told my closed-minded friend. "After ostracizing and smearing him behind his back, they'll be back for more in a week. I'm beginning to think they're all a bunch of crazy characters, not only he. Look at him now! Doesn't he look lonely and unhappy sitting there by himself. I sort of feel sorry for him now even if I don't like his ideas."

Surprisingly, my friend spoke sympathetically, "Me too. Now that they've gone I have a feeling of being in the calm that follows the storm—strange isn't it?"

I felt elated as I proposed, "Come on, Professor, let's have another cup of coffee and join him. We need a storm once in a while to drive us out of our stagnant rut. Besides, my ego may hate to admit it, but maybe he's got something in his ideas. Let's be different for a change; let's listen and try to find out what's right with his system rather than assume that it's all wrong."

"You know," murmured my paradoxical friend, "ever since you began talking about our so-called character, I thought we had a budding Plato who should be encouraged. But, you know how it is, I thought you were antagonistic toward him—so why break up a good friendship by disagreeing with you."

"Why you old hypocrite!" I retorted, slapping him on the back, "take it from this hypocrite, I always secretly admired him for his original thinking and for his fighting against overwhelming resistance. But you know how it is; I suppose I had to maintain professional superiority by belittling his ideas. Besides, I thought you expected my critical remarks in the way you introduced him as an 'odd character.'"

After joining our "character" at his table I indicated an interest in his system. I never expected the answer I received.

"You know," he almost whispered with relief in his eyes, "until now, no one has ever indicated an interest in my system. Every bit of resistance increased my aggressiveness. Now, your sudden interest and lack of resistance takes a weight off my shoulders. I hope you will understand, but my desire to impress others with my system has suddenly disappeared."

He left two bewildered professors scratching their heads over three hot coffees.
Thus:

What is believed today was once resisted.

Creators are "insane" until they acquire fame.

When creators are analyzed, their ideas are not; when ideas are analyzed, their creators are not.

THE SPECIFIC GENERALITY

(On the progressive range of goals and unified principles)

Three professors were having their social coffee during an intermission between classes. Their conversation turned to methods of inspiring students to indicate more scholastic effort.

The philosophy professor whose broad perspective perceived things in broad generalities and abstract principles said, "All activity is based on achieving goals. All students must be inspired by goals to achieve."

The psychology professor whose narrow perspective perceived things in narrow details and concrete facts said, "You are too dogmatic and show ignorance in saying 'all.' You have made an all-inclusive generality that is too vague and cannot be applied in any sensible discussion. We must be specific and concrete in making such statements. Let me say specifically that individual activity, both mental and physical, is based on preventing frustrations, or in overcoming the conflicts, barriers, and resistances to the achievement of the specific individual's goals."

The historian whose views were more flexible between the extremes of abstract principle and concrete fact said, "I think we all agree to that, but we must not forget that political and national acivity is based on achieving municipal and national goals."

"Let me repeat," said the bored philosopher, "all spiritual, mental, and physical activity is based on achieving goals. And now that we are all agreed on this generality, let us proceed to specify how we can apply it to the individual."

Thus:

What applies in principle to the individual applies in principle to the family, group, city, nation, and civilization.

Scientific facts induce to philosophical principles from which are deduced scientific facts.

Minor facts integrate to major principles; major principles integrate to unified principles.

THE PARADOX OF TRUTH

(On truth and unified principles)

The young college freshman, floating in the cloudy world of abstractions, peered intently thru his horn-rimmed glasses at his philosophy teacher. He was learning how minor facts integrate to become a major fact, how major facts integrate to become a concept, and how concepts integrate to become a principle. Being an intelligent student with an alert and creative mind he advanced this idea one step further and concluded to the professor, "If that is true, then we should be able to integrate all principles into a unified principle."

The philosophy professor's emotional ego, contrary to his rational wish, was irked by the "know it all" attitude of this brilliant student. He decided to put him in his proper place. Also, wishing to provoke his students into profound thought, he ignored the basic proposition and answered cryptically, "You used the word 'all'; 'all' means without exception. We cannot unify *all* principles into a unified principle no more than a big box can hold all boxes without holding itself."

This dimmed the bright student for a moment but he finally saw the light and restated his proposition, "Well, then, leaving out the word 'all,' this must be the truth: Principles can be integrated to a unified principle."

The provocative professor, still playing mental gymnastics said, "But everything is relative to time, place, individual, circumstance, and degree. Therefore, this new principle must be relative to something. If it is relative to something outside of itself, then it cannot integrate all things, for there will be some relative thing outside itself."

The exasperated student, whirling in the complex confusion of conflict, lost his patience and burst out with, "Then there is no truth if everything is relative!"

The philosophic professor laughed playfully to ease the sullen student's tension and said, "But if your statement about there being no truth is true, then the fact that there is no truth is a truth."

The suffering student felt he had an opportunity to avenge his persecuting professor when he said, "But your statement is too general to be true in all cases."

The sophisticated professor was not to be outwitted so easily by this naive student. "If that is so," he said, "then the statement you have just made is too general to be true in all cases, and maybe my case is the exception."

The incoherent, confused student finally quit in frustrated fury. "Well, you have convinced me," he said, "I know nothing!"

The satisfied professor beamed triumphantly and said to his penitent pupil, "If you admit you know nothing, then you must be a wise person. If you know you know nothing, then surely you know that. Then just as surely you do know something."

"So what!" asked the dazed, unilluminated student. "So what does all this prove?"

"It proves," said the professor, who was happy to end the strain on his brain, "that if you waste your time in sophistic arguments, as we have just done, you will end up knowing nothing except that you know nothing."
Thus:

Truth is limited by its own contradictions.

To see a negative truth is to see the unknown positive truth.

A truth that proves nothing is worth nothing.

THE WISE SCHOLAR

(On education and unified principles)

An intellectual student resolved to become the wisest of
scholars by seeking to acquire ultimate wisdom. He would
dedicate his life to teaching the ignorant masses and enlightening mankind. To prepare for this noble cause he
learned millions of facts covering hundreds of fields of
knowledge. After twenty years of research, study, meditation, and experimentation, he became a Doctor of Education.

In his studies he had refined all his factual knowledge
down to a few basic principles that enabled him to claim
possession of the purest of wisdom. His knowledge and
wisdom were supreme for they could not be distilled to a
purer essence. He had integrated and unified knowledge
and wisdom to get at the very source of knowledge. He was
a wise man indeed. The world had need for such knowledge as he would impart to it.

His profound wisdom was summed up in a few principles which he expressed in terms of proverbs, aphorisms,
maxims, and axioms. One of these profundities was, "Everything is relative." But when he attempted to apply this
essence of truth while teaching as a university professor,
he could not express any of his wisdom because his proverbs, aphorisms, maxims, and axioms were so dogmatic they
contradicted his principle of relativity. No one could ever

bear to listen an hour to the facts he could give to substantiate his dogmatic truths. So he never could express or prove the truth of relativity which lay behind all his dogmatic proverbial principles.

He had learned that, "Teachers should be democratic, not autocratic and dogmatic." All his principles could only be expressed dogmatically, so he had to sacrifice these principles in order to be a good teacher. He would not degrade the honor of his position by teaching dogmatically to his students. In practicing this principle he suggested to his students, "It is not for me to tell you what you should learn or to dictate what is right and wrong; you must make your own decisions." His disciples accepted these wise words with humble faith. They democratically decided to study the laws of nature. They democratically decided that the best means to do this was to get away from dull, analytical reading of text books and to study nature in reality at the seashore. Of course, they democratically decided that nature created warm sand to relax in. They further decided democratically that swimming and playing in the water was related to the physical and social nature of man. Not being autocratic, the learned professor had to accept their decision to "learn by doing." So his practical students learned the laws of nature by relaxing in the warm sand and by swimming and playing in the ocean water.

This wisest and most learned of all professors had learned that "The wisest are the most humble." This was one wise principle that he could practice. He had such a sincere sense of humility that he would never admit to knowing more than the lowest of his students. Thus none of his students, not even the dullest, ever did learn what the wise man himself had learned. As we leave this greatest of wise men some of his students are democratically deciding that he is more ignorant than they are.

In the basement below the wise professor's classroom an illiterate janitor was taking time off from shoveling coal into a furnace. This uneducated janitor took time off to dogmatically and authoritatively boast of his knowledge of furnaces to a curious student. On the base of this new knowledge the entranced youth, who was ignorant of furnaces, was already dreaming of and planning a newer and better furnace to benefit mankind.

Thus:

A talking fool with one fact teaches more than a silent wise man with a million.

The scholar's hoarded knowledge has no more value than the miser's money.

History's wisemen, creators, and leaders were not usually professors.

THE JIGSAW PUZZLE

(On progressive range perspective and unified principles)

A certain king was disturbed after seeing a TV movie about the decline and fall of the Roman Empire. Speaking at a conference of the world's foremost professors in their fields he said, "The state of the nation seriously concerns me. I have called this conference to have you renowned professors explain why other nations and civilizations have declined to ruin and disappeared."

The philosopher was first to speak and said in his broad, abstract, universal terms, "Civilizations decline when common spiritual, intellectual, and moral values are degenerated and displaced by individual material, physical, and sensual values. When common moral values no longer integrate a civilization, the civilization disintegrates."

The historian disagreed and spoke in terms of the nation. "Nations obviously fail because what happened to the Roman Empire parallels what happens in this nation. When nations fail to heed the lessons of history that repeat themselves, then nations decline and fall."

But the sociologist disagreed with the historian and spoke in terms of the group. "I disagree with the historian, for nations decline and fall when social equality degrades and destroys self-betterment groups. The absence of social pressure by superior groups in a declining nation causes the release of inhibitions. This deteriorates civilized manners and formal etiquette to degrade civilized man to the level of beggars and beasts."

The psychologist disagreed with the sociologist and spoke in terms of the individual. "What the sociologist has said is not true for in reality nations decline and fall when individuals fail to properly adjust to a society that becomes ever more complex. These maladjusted individuals disintegrate themselves from society to become solitary and neurotic recluses and hermits."

The biologist disagreed with all the professors and spoke in terms of the human body. "I think you are all wrong," he said, "for nations decline and fall simply because the luxurious wealth, debilitating diets, devitalizing vices, and easy cultural living of their degenerating Golden Age makes their bodies soft and their minds weak."

The economist could not be different and speaking in terms of wealth he also disagreed with all. "Obviously," he said, "you all fail to perceive what is apparent to all who must buy their bread in order to live. The fact is that nations decline and fall for no other reason than that they spend to excess and cannot maintain what has already been built up. When nations run out of wealth with which to produce an expanding economy, they do not expand; they contract."

The political-geographer spoke last and rendered his expected disagreement in terms of material resources. "All of you fail to realize," he said, "that without natural resources nations do not rise. When they fail to conserve natural resources, when they dissipate natural resources, they can no longer sustain their society. Then they decline and fall."

The wise king who heard these seven foremost experts disagree on the same subject interjected with a conclusion. "All you wise men speak great truths. All of you are right, yet all of you are wrong. Each of you holds only a part of the whole jigsaw puzzle that explains life. Each part of the jigsaw puzzle by itself means nothing; all the parts when separated mean nothing. Therefore we must integrate these disintegrated parts to a unified picture. We must perceive how each part relates to the whole. But how can we do this?"

The seven professors worked as a unified team for a full week in their attempt to evolve a unified picture of their separate branches of knowledge, but to no avail.

Becoming impatient, the king contacted another well-known expert—his ten year old son, an expert in putting jigsaw puzzles together. The royal father asked his princely son, "How do you manage to place so many odd pieces of your jigsaw puzzle together so easily?"

The young expert, looking up from his jigsaw puzzle on the floor said, "It is easy, Dad, I simply find one piece of the puzzle which contains something I know, such as a horse's head. Then I find all the parts related to this, such as the legs and body. With a picture of a horse in my mind it is a simple matter to put the parts of the horse together."

"Well," said the king, "You make me proud of you because of your expert answer, but how would you put this puzzle together?" And the king went on to explain the seven different parts of the professors' knowledge that made up his jigsaw puzzle.

The ten year old expert thought for a moment and replied, "The key is in what the philosopher said regarding the degeneration of moral values, for all other answers have failure of moral character as their basis. When I add the other six causes of the decline and fall of nations to this common moral basis, I derive a unified picture that looks like a tree. The root of this tree is moral character. As the root decays, so do all the branches of the tree. As moral character degenerates, so do all its historical, sociological, psychological, economical, political, and geographical branches decay."

The king thought he had found the answer he sought,

and being a wise and fair king, he rewarded all the experts who had assisted in the solution. He gave riches, titles, and jigsaw puzzles to the professors. To his son he gave an extra large ice cream cone which was appreciated with a happy smile.

Thus:

Destroy the root to destroy the branches; destroy moral character to destroy the individual, family, group, city, nation, and civilization.

Many minor causes make a major effect.

We perceive what we are prepared to perceive.

A PROVERBIAL PARABLE

(On the balancing trinity and unified principles)

In a discussion on the value of truth a wise man was asked what he considered to be the highest form of truth. He replied, "Eternal and universal truths are told in proverbs that are true in all ages and all places."

A radical who was prepared to perceive change in all things said, "I agree, for what could be truer than these proverbs: Change in all things is sweet. To be happy, constantly change. Change of pasture makes fat calves. He knows much who travels much. Obviously these proverbs prove that it is best to constantly change."

A reactionary who was prepared to perceive why there should be no change said, "I also agree, for what can be truer than these proverbs: Change is not made without regret. Happy is he who knows his good fortune and avoids change. The grass only looks greener in other pastures. It is better to turn back than to go astray. Evidently these proverbs prove that it is best not to change things."

A conservative who was prepared to perceive moderate changes in all things said, "I also agree, for what could be truer than these proverbs: That change is best which avoids the extreme. Happiness is a station between two little and too much change. He travels best who knows when to return. Travel makes a wise man better and a fool worse.

Apparently these proverbs prove that only moderate change is good."

Then the wise man said, "You all speak the great truths of proverbs, yet you contradict each other. But you speak a greater truth if you integrate your conflicting truths into a unified truth. For truth is a trinity of positive, neutral, and negative values. To quote proverbial wisdom: Times change; our truths change with them. Thus the radical who now believes in change will one day be a reactionary who believes in resisting radicals who would change his improved status. To again quote proverbs: All things change, yet nothing perishes. Likewise truth may change in part but not in the whole of its trinity. The true temperature of water in a glass may change from hot to warm to cold, but the greater truth remains unchanged; it is still a glass of water."

Thus:

A proverb is a principle derived from millions of facts.

There are three sides to every story—your side, my side, and the best side.

Truth is a trinity of positive, neutral, and negative values.

THE GARDEN OF LOVE

(On the progressive range of love and unified principles)

"All the world loves a lover," quoted the great poet. "And heaven does too," said the Angel Gabriel. So a special Garden of Love was established in heaven for the greatest of lovers.

Casanova, the great lover, argued, "I should be awarded the honor of basking in the Garden of Love, for does not the world of women consider me the greatest of lovers?"

This claim to fame was drowned in a roar of unloving protest from malevolent males who disagreed.

Casanova, still laughing as the roar ebbed to a mutter, turned to Gabriel and said mockingly, "Ha! Ha! Are these pitiful creatures lovers! Are they greater than I, the great Casanova? Look at them! Look at that withered, old graybeard; at that fanatically tense radical; at that uncultured and harried husband; at that frigid, superior snob, and at that bloated dissipate. These things are lovers! Ho! Ho!"

He was interrupted by rumblings of hate and vengeance paradoxically coming from the lips of the greatest lovers.

Gabriel, guardian of the Garden of Love, exclaimed, "Hold on now! Let us be fair and just. Let each of you state your claim and I shall judge which of you is the greatest of the great lovers. If you will line up I will sit in judgment to decide your case."

There was a panicky scramble to be first in line. The

sensualist lovers galloped uninhibitedly and were first in line. The intellectual lovers trotted with moderation and were next in line. The spiritual lovers walked with dignity to be last in line.

The aesthetic epicurean was first to speak. Smacking his sensuous lips, he purred, "I love fine-flavored foods, delicious drinks, fragrant perfumes, and beautiful women to tenderly caress. These are loves to work for and to enjoy."

"I have a greater love than that," enunciated the elegant egotist as he sensuously caressed his soft curls with delicate finger tips. "I love myself. I love my beautiful features, my exquisite manners, and all the superior qualities which make me the envy of the common herd. What other lover gives such tender loving care and works so affectionately for his love?"

The friendly platonic lover answered in a note of disgust, "Your degrading, selfish, sensual love cannot compare with my unselfish brotherly love. I love my friend for his mental brilliance, not his sensual beauty. We are united by common ideas, not opposing physiques. I would gladly work and fight for this love of my friend."

"Paternal love is much greater than that," said the proud parent making tender passes at the heads of children who were not there. "I love my children above all else. Cold reason may guide this love, but it is balanced by the warmth of emotional sentiment. Only the family can have so much love—paternal love, maternal love, and filial love. Only family love can unite different children to fight and even die for it."

"Greater love hath no man than his country," quoted the tense patriot. "I love my country with a fervid, patriotic love. I am not only willing to work and fight for my Fatherland, but also to die for it."

"I too will work, fight, and die for my love," said the religious theist. My devotion is based on pure spiritual love. I love my God, the Greatest of the Great, and as no one is greater, there is no greater love. Therefore, I am a greater lover than all of you."

A wise old man, claiming no title of love except that of philosopher, was last to be judged by Gabriel. This wise man socratically questioned, "What love is greater than the love of wisdom? Can any feeling or sentiment of love be more magnificent and significant than that of visualizing the whole vista of love thru the progressively broadening ranges of society? Can any love be more profound than that of perceiving the amazing integration and unity of spiritual, intellectual, and sensual love? Only love of wisdom enables one to perceive the awe-inspiring significance of love's effect in inspiring and unifying man's spiritual, mental, and physical activity to give him a reason for being. Only love of wisdom can conceive of human love synchronizing in unity with the complex cycles and balances of Nature. Only love of wisdom can reveal how man and Nature, and all things spiritual, intellectual, and sensual are unified by the ultimate creator of all, by the ultimate unity —God."

The joyous pulse of heaven stopped as a strange silence enraptured all in that Holy Place. It was the silence of awe-inspiring truth whose dignity could not be besmirched by profane argument.

Gabriel gently broke the silence in a hushed tone of reverence. "I may be prejudiced by these profound heavenly truths in making my judgment; but Casanova, let me ask you: What is love? Are you, a lover of woman, a greater lover than a lover of a pet, a lover of wisdom, or a lover of God?"

"What can I say," mumbled the humbled Casanova, "after what the wise man said regarding the love of wisdom I feel I never should have opened my big mouth. I deserve to feel ridiculous and insignificant relative to this honorable lover of wisdom—the indisputable one entitled to being the greatest of lovers."

"Well," said Gabriel a little lost for words at this change in Casanova. "Well, is there anyone else to dispute the wise man's being the greatest lover, even tho he himself has made no claim to it?"

Gabriel saw only bowed heads nodding negatively; all he heard was silence.

"Then I will make my judgment," Gabriel said. "All have the same quantity of love, but all differ in the quality of that love. All of your love is good, but I think you will agree that love which encompasses the most love is the greatest. And from what you have heard, the selfish sensualist loves the fewest; the intellectual loves more, and the spiritual lover encompasses the most. Also, because man will work for sensual love, work and fight for intellectual love, and work, fight, and die for spiritual love, I would say that man considers sensual love to be the least valued and spiritual love to be the most valued."

No one disagreed with this judgment so Gabriel went on to define his heavenly plan for the Garden of Love.

The sensual lovers would be gardeners of the grounds in the Garden. Their senses would be thrilled by the heavenly pleasures of seeing, smelling, feeling, touching, and tasting the once forbidden fruit.

The intellectual lovers would be the architects and overseers over the Garden. From atop a hill they would look down at undulating fields or up at billowing clouds to let their minds rapturously wander in imaginative dreams.

The spiritual lovers would be placed within a halo of stardust and sunbeams to float in the pure ecstasy of love. Their radiations would warm and enlighten the entire Garden of Love.

A special place was reserved for the lover of wisdom. His wisdom encompassed all love, whether spiritual, intellectual, or sensual, so he was to judge new lovers and assign them to their proper place in the Paradise that was the Garden of Love.

Thus:

Love upgrades from the sensual to the intellectual to the spiritual, and degrades in reverse.

Increase sensual love, and in balance, decrease intellectual and spiritual love.

Love is the universal, unifying goal to give man a reason for being and something to work, fight, and die for.

THE MULTITUDINOUS INDIVIDUAL

(On the progressive ranges of ideas and unified principles)

At an educational conference the basic needs of man were being discussed by a panel of experts.

The Doctor of Psychology suggested this theory: "The individual is subconsciously motivated by self-survival, then personal success, and then egocentric pleasure."

The Doctor of Social Science based his report on statistical data. He said, "The group is unconsciously influenced by pressures of surviving as a minority, then of achieving success as a majority, then by the pleasures of social activities."

The Doctor of Contemporary History referred to facts when he said, "This nation was born to struggle for survival, then to compete for success, and now to indulge in cultural pleasures."

The Doctor of Philosophy offered this opinion: "Civilizations follow a cyclical pattern of surviving to enable success which enables pleasure. Pleasure degrades the civilization which returns to survival conditions."

When the applause for the panel members had subsided the chairman of the conference said, "Let us commend these erudite panel members for their profound views on the basic needs of man. The multitudinous aspects and complexity of this problem are apparent in considering each expert perceived this problem differently. Such conditions make it difficult to solve this problem without a panel of well-known experts such as these."

A wise, old teacher, without degrees or titles, for he was too busy teaching and learning to acquire them, was asked his layman's opinion of the experts' reports. He said, "Apparently, from what all the panel members said, what applies in principle to the individual also applies in principle to the family group, city, nation, and civilization—or to all the progressive ranges of society. All gave a common principle which stated that the basic needs of man follow in the general order of survival, success, and pleasure. This common principle differed among the speakers only in the broader or narrower perspective of time and space. If all agreed on this principle, why complicate and confuse this problem by having a panel of experts argue over what they agree on?"

A murmur of resentment stirred the assembly. An angry voice above the rest demanded, "Mr. Chairman, what degree or position entitles this person to inform us what we should know or do?"

The chairman, respecting parliamentary procedure, permitted the wise teacher to continue. "The same principles apply," the teacher said, "to all educational fields and to all the progressive ranges of society. So when the word 'individual' is seen or heard in a sentence we can substitute the words 'family, group, city, nation, and civilization' and still retain the same meaning. The principle would be the same but the facts would differ in perspective of time and space."

A rumble of protest perked up the professors, but no one could justify this protest by words so the teacher continued: "On this principle, if the psychologist wrote a book on the nature of the individual, we could replace the word 'individual' with the word 'family' or 'group' to have a book on sociology. The same could be done to have a book on politics, history, or philosophy. So, in principle, a psychology book can also be a sociology, a history, and a philosophy book simultaneously. An individual could read one book, then re-read it in terms of another range of society. He could read four books on four subjects from one book on one subject. Thus, in terms of common principles, many books may be unified within one."

A roar of reaction rolled round the rows of the assembly like an ominous storm. The professionals foresaw this idea destroying their professional vocabulary and their professional literature. It could destroy them as the experts who translated and interpreted their professional jargon.

The psychologist exploded in a release of repressed inhibitions. "That principle could never be adjusted to the level of the individual!"

The sociologist screamed with mob-like fury, "That principle could never be integrated within different group levels!"

The historian bellowed in panic at this revolutionary crisis, "I have never heard of such a principle applied in the realm of nations!"

The philosopher questioned the truth of the teacher's thesis. "How could a common principle apply to the pattern of such extremes as the individual and his civilization?"

The humble teacher let the rumble stumble to a mumble then fumbled the functionaries with this jumble. "If what you all say is true, then you all state a principle common to psychology, sociology, history, and philosophy. Well, gentlemen, you are either wrong in your individual statements, which will make me wrong; or you are right in your collective statements which will make me right. Now which is it?"

None of the professors would admit he was wrong individually, so they had to admit the teacher was right. But they did not want to admit he was right so they had to say they were wrong collectively.

The meeting broke up in bedlam with the psychologist seeking his psychiatrist to resolve his mental conflict. The others sought aspirins, sedatives, and alcohol to dissolve this problem and their headaches.

Thus:

What applies in principle to the individual applies in principle to the progressive ranges of society—the individual, family, group, city, nation, and civilization.

Principles differ only in relative facts of time, space, individual, circumstance, and degree.

All the sciences use different words and facts to apply the same principles.

THE UNITY OF OPPOSITES

(On the progressive range of society and unified principles)

It was Judgment Day and those who would enter the pearly gates were asked the same question: "You were placed on earth to accomplish some good; now what good did you accomplish?"

The good mother said, "I set standards to guide and unite the individuals in my family into a strong, united family."

The respected leader said, "And I set standards to unite and guide the opposing parents in my group."

The elected mayor said, "And I set standards to unite and guide the opposing leaders in my city."

The powerful king said, "I also set standards to guide and unite the opposing mayors in my nation."

And the wise philosopher said, "I set standards to guide and unite the opposing kings in our civilization."

The pearly gate-keeper was well satisfied with these answers, but he asked one more question. "But who is beyond this point? Who sets the standards to guide and unify the opposing philosophies in your world?"

A mystic who appeared to desire to be alone in meditation said, "Opposing philosophers in our world are guided and unified by the unifier of all opposites, by the unity without opposites, by the source of all opposites, by the ultimate end of all things."

The pearly gate-keeper smiled at this cryptic, mystic message, and said, "Welcome, Brothers, you have reached the ultimate goal where there is no opposite."

Thus:

Families unite under parents; groups unite under leaders; cities unite under mayors; nations unite under kings; civilizations unite under a spiritual unity.

Everyone guides and unites someone; everyone is guided and united by someone.

All things integrate to unity; all things are from one.

THE KEYSTONE OF INFINITY

*(On the progressive range of knowledge
and unified principles)*

The world's foremost scholars and authorities in their particular fields of knowledge decided to hold a conference. The purpose of this brilliant array of brains was to achieve better understanding of knowledge in general. To do this they would attempt to interrelate their different fields of knowledge into a structural pattern. With such an interrelated structure they would have the means to make all their knowledge parts of one knowledge. With this unified structure they could integrate their different principles to derive a unified principle. This unified principle would enable the simplest answer to enable the greatest understanding of God, nature, and man.

Those scholars whose fields of knowledge required the broadest perspective were permitted to speak first, for the nature of their subject involved all. Those scholars whose fields required the narrowest perspective spoke last, for their fields involved the least.

The philosopher said, "To understand the universe, we must understand its civilizations."

The historian said, "To understand the world, understand the civilizations that compose it."

The Statesman said, "To understand the civilization we must understand the nations that compose it."

The politician said, "To understand the nation, we must understand its cities."

The sociologist said, "To understand the city, understand its groups."

The psychologist said, "To understand the group, understand the individuals within it."

The physiologist said, "To understand the human individual we must understand the animal."

The biologist said, "To understand animals we must understand insects."

The bacteriologist said, "To understand insects we must understand bacteria."

The logician said, "To understand the complex we must first understand the simpler parts that compose it."

The mystic who was there only as an invited guest, because his knowledge was such that it could not be reasoned, perceived, or experimented with, was the last to speak. He said, "Some levels of knowledge can only be grasped by faith. Sometimes we must believe what we cannot prove by logic or perception. Thus, we must believe that a Keystone holds this integrated order and unified structure of knowledge together. For without the Keystone, the structure disintegrates into its separate unconnected parts. To understand this Keystone, we must understand the universe. And if we understand the Keystone we will better understand the purest essence of all things, the purest of spirit which holds mind and matter together."

The chairman of the conference, who was a physical scientist, interrupted this outburst to say, "What is all this mumbo-jumbo about faith, Keystone, structure, and spirit. If we cannot see this Keystone with our eyes or mind, but must believe it on blind faith, then I think it is ridiculous. I could just as well say to believe me when I say the Keystone that holds knowledge together is a piece of green cheese. This Keystone to integrate and unify knowledge is nonsense. It is superstitious semantics that has no place at a scientific meeting. I cannot tolerate it, so I am quitting as chairman of this meeting and am going back to my laboratory."

When the chairman, who was the keystone of that conference, left the meeting, the conference disintegrated into separate individuals who were glad to get home. For it seemed that what each had to say had no connection with what others had to say. There was no chairman to integrate and unify their different fields of knowledge.

Thus:

To understand the whole, understand the parts.

Beyond the sensory is the rational; beyond the rational is the mystic.

Remove the keystone and the whole structure tumbles.

THE PHILOSOPHER'S STONE

(On the progressive range of ideas and unified principles)

Beyond the beyond, in the Philosopher's Paradise, there stood a large, jewel-like stone radiating a strange, golden luminescence. This was the legendary "Philosopher's Stone." Men of earth wrote of it in their books of alchemy and philosophy. This was the elusive stone they sought but never found. No wonder it was sought; it was purported to be capable of turning baser metals into gold.

In paradise, where all good dreams come true, the philosophers had their dreams and destiny fulfilled. They had finally found the Philosopher's Stone. Like the Blarney Stone of Ireland which opened one's mouth to make him witty, the Philosopher's Stone opened one's mind to make him wise. This was true if for no other reason than being an attraction like the corner drugstore. It was a meeting place to attract idle bodies to activate minds by common talk.

As will happen in any paradise, a group sat around the Philosopher's Stone to indulge in the eternal happiness of their paradise. These lovers of wisdom were freely discussing and openly debating answers to that eternal and limitless philosophical question—Why?

"Why were we chosen to enter this paradise?" asked a sagacious sage.

The Stone Age philosopher, admiring the crystalline qualities of the Philosopher's Stone, came out of his meditating trance to answer, "Do you suppose it is because each of us has made a contribution to wisdom? It was I who first made the unknown known, and so unfeared, by giving it a name. I named those objects we can see, such as 'pine' and 'oak,' 'rose' and 'lilac.' Imagine how impossible it was to think or communicate until I created these words which I called 'facts.'"

"You certainly did contribute to wisdom," replied the Iron Age philosopher. "Maybe I was selected for extending and broadening your facts into a unified idea called a 'concept.' These concepts enabled thought about abstract ideas rather than concrete things. They dealt with the form of things rather than with the thing itself. Since that day, man could think of things in general that did not actually exist, rather than of a specific thing that did exist. I symbolized these concepts by such key words as 'tree' and 'bush.'"

"That was a major advance in wisdom," exclaimed the Ancient Greek philosopher, "but your ideas were still rather narrow-minded relative to my broader ideas. I integrated and unified your facts and concepts into a broader and more abstract idea which I called a 'principle.' These principles manifested a common element in different things to make them similar. My key word 'plant' symbolizes a principle which integrates and unified the facts of the pine and the oak, and the concepts of the tree and the bush. Three of my principles, namely 'plant,' 'animal,' and 'mineral' summed up all knowledge heretofore learned. This made deductive reasoning possible, for how else could man deduce facts from principles without the principles."

"Yes, that was a revolutionary advance in the mind of man," agreed the Ancient Roman philosopher. "On the same principle I believe I am here for developing and broadening the ideas of all the wise philosophers who came before me. I thus discovered the 'major principle.' This integrated and unified your previous facts, concepts, and principles. These dealt with material things we can see—

with plants, animal, and minerals. I symbolized my major principle by the key word 'nature' which is a sub-branch of the branch of knowledge called science. This major principle enabled man to think in terms of the world and the universe, not just in terms of plant, animal, and mineral."

"I should be more modest," said the Medieval Age philosopher, "but I too extended what others did, and I also discovered a major principle. I integrated and unified facts, concepts and principles of revealed, spiritual truths that cannot be seen—about the Holy Father, the Holy Son, and the Holy Spirit. My major principle integrated and unified the mystical hierarchy of God's world and man's relationship to it. The key word symbolizing this major principle is 'God.' He is studied in that branch of knowledge called theology. This major principle enabled man to think in terms of that broader spiritual world beyond the material world."

"I too discovered a major principle," the Renaissance philosopher informed the group, "but I unified facts, concepts, and principles that could be intellectually reasoned. These dealt with man and his social, political, and economic organizations. They are symbolized by the word 'humanism' which is a sub-branch of the branch of knowledge called philosophy. This major principle enabled the perception of the rational and progressive order of social development. It enabled a better understanding of the relationship between man and the different ranges of his society."

As the topic progressively developed and broadened it was logical to anticipate that the Modern philosopher would be next in order. It was logical in the progressive order of ideas to predict his answer. "It was I," he said, "who first discovered an ideal form common to all branches of nature, not just one branch. I discovered that trees, watersheds, and deltas; the blood and the nervous systems, and so forth, have a trunk from which progressively extend major branches and minor branches. This common form was a means to integrating and unifying the many specific principles of nature into a 'unified principle.' I symbolized this unified principle by the key phrase, 'structural form.' This unified principle of nature enabled the mind of man to grasp the whole fundamental order of Nature's universe. It was like the difference between learning of a country's topography by volumes of books, or by simply looking at a single map. This, in my estimation, was the ultimate wisdom for it advanced the mind of man to the broadest of ranges possible."

A stranger, appearing as if he had just come in from a long journey, entered the discussion. "Not so, Modern Man," he interjected, "since you left that shrinking world of ours I broadened your unified principle to one which not only unified the laws of Nature, but also the laws of God and Man. This was nothing unusual for I only extended and broadened what you and other philosophers before me had progressively extended and broadened."

"But how could you possibly have done that?" exclaimed the Modern philosopher.

"I perceived," said the Future Age philosopher, "that the facts, concepts, principles, major principles, and unified principles up to my age had one thing in common. Like the framework which is common to all houses, there is a framework which is common to all knowledge and wisdom. Not only in science, but in theology and philosophy, the common form is like a tree. Like a tree it has a trunk from which progressively extend branches and sub-branches. This unified principle could be called the 'tree of knowledge,' 'the tree of wisdom,' 'the tree of life,' or any other kind of tree. But many kinds of trees would have to be listed to entail a tree for each branch of knowledge. I read in my books on earth that the Iron Age philosopher had unified many kinds of natural trees and bushes by one key word—

'plant.' On the same principle I unified many trees, which symbolized principles, under one key title. Using words common to all these symbolic trees I called my unified principle the 'progressive range principle.' "

"But how can this benefit man's mind?" interrupted the Modern philosopher.

The Future Age philosopher replied, "This unified principle manifests the progressively broadening ranges of any development in the world of God, Nature, or Man. It gives, not only a road map of the world of matter, but also of the worlds of the mind and of the spirit. It enables one map to manifest how three different worlds are integrated within a unified entity. This unified principle is like one map of a city which shows not only the highways on the surface, but also the subways beneath and the airways above. This enables an integrated, unified perspective of three different levels as they effect each other. Is not this the ultimate wisdom? Can we possibly go beyond this?"

A moment of silent reflection was disturbed by a mighty voice booming into the ether. "Is this the question of a philosopher? In this world without end, is there an end to the discovery of wisdom? In reaching the end we go no further; we only go backward. This may not be so bad, as proven by your discussion, to get better balance and perspective. In reaching the end we can perceive more only if we are prepared to perceive more."

It was the telepathic voice of the Future-future Philosopher. It was beamed to contact the spirits of the philosophers thru the medium of extra-sensory perception. Contact was then lost and nothing else was said. But as words failed, a strange symbol appeared wavering in the radiant beams of the Philosopher's Stone. The cryptic symbol took the form of an inverted tree. The word "God" appeared where the roots would be.

After excitedly discussing this mystic symbol the philosophers concluded: This truly was the culminating step on the ladder of wisdom's progress. One symbolic diagram was worth a thousand symbolic words. It enabled man to apply the progressive range principle to better teach and learn any branch or sub-branch of the tree of knowledge. It was truly the ultimate wisdom in revealing the sources of knowledge and in considering God the Ultimate Limit to the progressive ranges of society and nature—the Ultimate Principle of all unified principles.

Putting the mystic symbol to practical application, one of the philosophers drew a picture on the heavenly cloud beneath his feet. Each in turn added trim to this Christmas-like tree. The result:

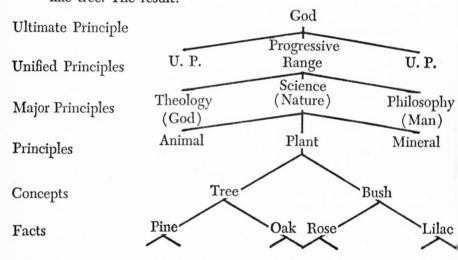

Ultimate Principle		God	
Unified Principles	U. P.	Progressive Range	U. P.
Major Principles	Theology (God)	Science (Nature)	Philosophy (Man)
Principles	Animal	Plant	Mineral
Concepts		Tree	Bush
Facts	Pine	Oak Rose	Lilac

The Progressive Range Principle

The Renaissance philosopher had an idea that all things in the worlds of God, Nature, and Man followed a principle of 'balance.' He believed all ranges of the progressive range were balanced between negative and positive limits with neutral degrees between. He made a mobile of some old wire coat hangers that were lying around to demonstrate what he meant. He manifested on the mobile how minor balances function within the broader influence of major balances. He showed, by tilting the mobile, how change in any one range of the progressive range causes balancing changes in all the other ranges.

He integrated this principle into the progressive range principle and suggested a unified symbol to enable greater integration and unity of knowledge. He drew a sketch of his progressive range of balances, and for simplification, labeled each balancing range according to the progressive ranges of society. It looked like this:

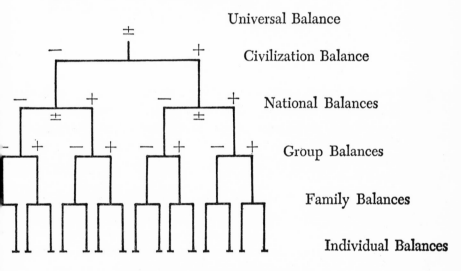

Universal Balance

Civilization Balance

National Balances

Group Balances

Family Balances

Individual Balances

Progressive Range of Balances

The Modern Philosopher had spent much of his time on earth dealing with the cycles of nature and with their relationship to the political, social, and economic cycles of man. He proposed that cycles be integrated within the progressive range symbol.

He explained that balancing changes are also cyclical changes. Thus minor cycles operated within the range of broader major cycles. This resulted in a progressive range of cycles. Also using the progressive range of society as an example he made this sketch:

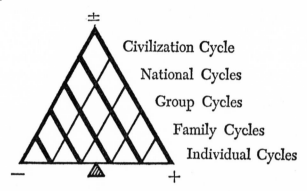

Progressive Range of Cycles

The light of wisdom radiated from the eyes of the philosophers as they happily left the radiance of the Philosopher's Stone. The truth of the Stone had at last been revealed to them. True, it did not turn baser metals into gold. That was only a symbolic expression of a truer meaning—it turned baser ideas into golden ideas. For one thing it had turned the baser ideas of why they were there to the golden idea of advancing the progress of wisdom.

Truly, the Philosopher's Stone, which many tried to find in their many different ways, inspired golden ideas. As the sun enlightened and unified the different activities of man, so the Philosopher's Stone enlightened mental activities of different men into a unified search of wisdom. Thus:

When the oak becomes a tree and the tree becomes a plant and the plant takes the form of man's growth, then the mind of man grows too.

Man, mind, and morals grow as facts unify to concepts and concepts unify to principles which unify to unified principles.

As the sun unifies the activity of man and nature, so God unifies knowledge and wisdom.

THE MUSIC CYCLE

(On the balance of music and the self-discipline cycle)

While surviving the holocaust of war a man had no time for music. Even if he had, music was destroyed in him by those realities of war which kill aesthetic senses and stifle sentimental emotions. He survived war to suffer the hardships that followed. His long-time fear and hopelessness made him pessimistic and morbid. But at their worst things can only change for the better. They did as deficiency of material things revealed spiritual values. Suffering misery inspired religious faith. Hopelessness in surviving on earth was balanced by hope of surviving beyond. This hope inspired self-disciplined determination and effort to forego present goals of temporary pleasure to achieve future goals of more permanent value. His only music was at church services and with fellow workers in the rhythm of mutual cooperation. Such deficiency, adversity, and faith molded a stern, self-disciplined religious man of moral character.

One day he was asked, "What kind of music do you like?"

This unsmiling religious person answered solemnly, "I like music that is spiritualistic, moralistic, universal, and eternal. I like music that expresses spiritual love, deals with sad tragedy, whose subject is God and his heavenly saints, and which is created for the church and the aristocracy. I sing the simple melody of folk songs in the minor key. This is slow in tempo and low in volume. Such music inspires my soul, teaches a moral, and develops my character."

The interrogator thanked him and bid him adieu.

Time changed the man's nature. His self-disciplined effort achieved the elation of success. Success permitted leisure to contemplate intellectual and cultural luxuries. As intellectual values increased, in balance, his spiritual values decreased. Intellectual and cultural goals, leisure and luxury softened his body, weakened his mind, and dulled his spirit. Success bred self-satisfaction and a lack of goals. Without goals he had no need for self-disciplined effort. To achieve the hope that goals inspire he supported idealistic goals of improving humanity at the balancing loss of improving himself. Success and leisure made him less dependent upon mutual cooperation for survival and success. The more he expressed independent personality, in balance, the less he expressed dependable character. Without self-disciplined character he was easily tempted by sensual pleasures to relieve the boredom of religious ceremony and cultural appreciation. As he lost spiritual values and decreased mental appreciations, in balance, he increased sensual pleasures. His philosophy of moderation between the extremes of excess and deficiency was not a practiced fact. He found less time for church music, more time for concerts, and a new interest in popular music. Such rational moderation molded a soft, sober, intellectually cultured personality and man of leisure who was again asked, "What kind of music do you like?"

This cultured person smiled and answered formally, "I like music that is intellectual, idealistic, nationalistic, and lifelong. I like music that expresses sentimental love, deals with sober drama, whose subject is nature and national heroes, and which is created for opera and the bourgeoisie. I play classic harmonies of composed folk songs in a balanced unity of the major and minor key. This is moderate in tempo and medium in volume. Such music affects my mind, teaches a principle, and develops my personality."

The interrogator thanked him and went on.

Boredom lies behind the principle of change in all human activity. Boredom with intellectual activities led to sensual activities and material things. The more he used sensory organs, in balance, the less he used his spiritual conscience and intellectual mind. His spiritual devotion had withered; his intellectual appreciation atrophied, and his sensual pleasures were dulling with dissipation. He had no time for church hymns, little time for theater concerts, and much time for nightclub rhythms. Again he was asked, "What kind of music do you like?"

The sociable person laughed and answered informally, "I like music that is sensual, realistic, individualistic, and ever-changing. I like music that expresses physical love, deals with gay comedy, whose subject is man and his personal loves, and which is created for the theater and the proletarian. I listen to complex rhythms of art songs in the major key, which are fast in tempo and loud in volume. Such music excites my senses, teaches nothing, and develops my popularity."

Again the interrogator thanked him and departed.

Excesses of intellectual appreciation caused him to seek erotic pleasures to stimulate deadened senses. When these bored him, he sought any change from monotony. Temporary pleasures to relieve boredom became his life goal. This required no self-disciplined determination and effort, for temptations became positive goals not to be denied by the negative conscience. In losing self-discipline he lost will power to resist dissipating his wealth and power on perverting pleasures. Eventually, perverting pleasures degraded him to the level of appreciating nothing, including music. Degradation and degeneracy led to his ruin. He became a moral, intellectual, and physical degenerate. As for music, he had none—he was too busy finding meals in order to survive.

The inquisitive interrogator who persisted in asking, "What kind of music do you like?" was an inquiring philosopher. He sought to know how and why music changed with man's nature. After following the changing nature of man and his music he collated facts to unify them into principles. To organize and simplify he listed musical values in columns relative to the man's nature as it changed—like this:

Negative Values	Neutral Values	Positive Values
spiritual	intellectual	sensual (material)
moralistic	idealistic	realistic
universal	nationalistic	individualistic
eternal	life-long	ever-changing
spiritual love	sentimental love	physical love
sad	sober	gay
tragedy	drama	comedy
God	Nature	Man
heavenly	national	personal
saint	hero	lover
church	opera	theater
aristocracy	bourgeoisie	proletarian
sing	play	listen
simple	classic	complex
melody	harmony	rhythm
folk song	composed folk song	art song
minor key	balanced major-minor key	major key
slow tempo	moderate tempo	fast tempo
low volume	medium volume	loud volume
inspires soul	effects mind	excites senses
teaches moral	teaches principle	teaches nothing
develops character	develops personality	develops popularity

Scanning this list he perceived startling coincidences and conceived novel conclusions. He saw an integrated relationship between the three columns which made them a unity of diverse negative, neutral, and positive values.

He perceived a parallel between the musical history of an individual and that of nations and civilizations. He concluded that music changes with the changing nature of the progressive ranges of society—the individual, family, group, city, nation, and civilization.

He placed the word "Medieval" over the negative column, "Renaissance" over the neutral column, and "Modern" over the positive column to manifest the chronological order of music in a cycle of civilization.

He further reasoned: Changes in music parallel changes in dancing. Music and dancing are arts; maybe the same principle applies to all arts—to painting, architecture, sculpturing, theater, literature, etc. He studied changes in art from the medieval to the renaissance to the modern age. He listed values stressed in each age under appropriate columns. Then he unified his facts to formulate this principle: The arts are integrated to a unity of balancing negative, neutral, and positive values. The unifying element in changing art is the nature of man as it changes from spiritual to intellectual to sensual values.

He was alarmed by the revelation that there were no other values than the negative, neutral, and positive. This meant that beyond the positive and sensual values of degeneration were the negative and spiritual values of regeneration. In between was degradation and ruin.

"Of what value is this knowledge?" asked the philosopher of himself. "The nature of modern man is positivistic, sensualistic, materialistic, and optimistic. He cannot perceive the balancing values of negativism, spiritualism, and pessimism beyond his rosy glasses. He ridicules prophets of doom and gloom, like gay drinkers who laugh at sad lessons told by fallen drunkards."

With stoic resignation he filed his report and forgot it.

That night a ragged beggar approached him. It was the degenerated subject of his report. The repentant sinner was now fanatically religious and liked minor key church hymns.

The philosopher left his morbid friend to revive his own depressed spirit at a tavern. Whiling away time he played a jukebox. What music did he play? Well, he liked the melody of church chorales to inspire his unity with mankind.

Better, he liked the harmony of classical symphonies for aesthetic appreciation and rational analysis. But he played a popular, jarring jungle rhythm—not that his nature liked it, but it was the only music available in his age.
Thus:

Music makes man's nature; man's nature makes his music.

As man's nature changes, so changes his art and his civilization.

To know man and his civilization, know his art and music.

THE UNIFIED PHILOSOPHY

(On symbolically integrating principles to a unified principle)

Around Mount Olympus, the home of good Greek Gods, there lived three spirits of former earthly Greek philosophers. They were still seeking to find a philosophy of philosophies, the basis of all philosophies, the basis of all wisdom, the ultimate philosophy. Heraclitus who was born first was given first choice in stating his thesis. He said, "I have studied all knowledge and integrated all of it into one principle. This principle states that all truth and wisdom are based on PROGRESSIVE, CONSTANT CHANGE."

Anaximander who was born later and had profited by the previous knowledge of Heraclitus said, "I have studied and integrated all philosophies into one principle. This principle states that all truth and wisdom are dependent upon PROGRESSIVE, CONSTANT, CYCLICAL CHANGE."

Aristotle who was born later had integrated his own wisdom to that of the previous two. He said, "I have also studied and integrated all philosophies into one principle. This one principle, derived from many different principles, states that truth and wisdom are determined by the 'Golden Mean' of PROGRESSIVE, CONSTANT, BALANCING, CYCLICAL CHANGE to MODERATE between the EXTREMES of excess and deficiency."

Heranaris, who was born after Aristotle, had gained his wisdom by studying all the previous philosophers. But he had been born into an age of materialistic philosophers. He had been exiled into oblivion by the contemporary scientific school of philosophy and his abstract philosophy remained unknown on earth. But the Gods see behind the folly of all men and gave Heranaris his just reward. They gave him membership in the Mount Olympus school of philosophy. Being true philosophers seeking wisdom, Heraclitus, Anaximander, and Aristotle let Heranaris speak.

This is what Heranaris said, "I have studied all of you who have integrated philosophies. I have studied you Heraclitus, you Anaximander, and you Aristotle. I have integrated all your philosophical principles into one unified principle that applies to both man and nature. This unified principle states that all truth and wisdom, whether they be spiritual, intellectual, or material in value, are one. It is a unified principle to bridge the gap between mystical, philosophical, and scientific knowledge. This unified principle formally states that all wisdom is based on PROGRESSIVE, CONSTANT, BALANCING, CYCLICAL CHANGE of a NEUTRAL VALUE between POSITIVE and NEGATIVE EXTREMES of an ENTITY."

"Eureka!" they all exclaimed, "We have found it! We have found the unified principle!"

Lifting Heranaris upon their shoulders they bore him triumphantly to the unified source of all the Greek Gods, to almighty Jove. Jove was so pleased at Heranaris's discovery of a secret known but to the Olympic gods that he forthwith bestowed upon him the official title of "Ph.D." or "Demi-god of Philosophy."

Thus:

Wisdom is a synthesis of thesis and antithesis.

Fact plus fact equals principle, plus principle equals unifying principle.

Truth is a neutral degree of difference between positive and negative values.

FINDING THE SOURCE OF KNOWLEDGE

(On the unified balancing trinity of civilization)

In the world beyond the beyond the Wisest of the Wise sat to judge three philosophers. He spoke: I have lived thru many changing ages and have listened to many wise men; now I sit to judge you three, the wisest philosophers of Western civilization. I ask each of you the age-old question: What is truth?"

The three philosophers, a 12th century medieval mystic, a 16th century renaissance intellectual, and a 20th century modern scientist, answered in the order they appeared in history. Each carried a volume of history to prove his evidence to be true.

The medieval mystic said, "Sir, we live in a predetermined world of God where man is born evil. Man must be controlled by disciplines set by religious authority. Their intuitive, supersensory, supernatural divine creations and revelations are expressed in mystic symbols. They are taught by spiritual, rhetorical sermons. These are preached by pious priests to listening meditators in the silent meditation of the monastery. We live by a moral code and the conscience of our soul. These spiritual guides form our unformed, stern, morbid, moral character. We believe in knowers who meditate on the meaning and diversity of ideas and doctrines. We believe in the theological, spiritualistic divinities that oppose science. We deductively reason to integrate knowledge into universal wholes."

Meanwhile a strange red character had appeared from nowhere. His horns and tail made him to be a creature of another world. Having listened, he rudely cut in, "By lucifer! How much of this can my boiling brain take!"

"Be quiet! You devil," said the Wise Judge.

Then the Wise Judge who knew all answers, past, present, and future, including the future answers of the philosophers said, "Now be patient until these three philosophers finish; then you will have revelations to make you blush even redder with ignorance."

The stern medieval mystic continued: "We live simple lives of deficiency as we inhibit desires by holy day fasts and abstinences. We believe and have faith in a spiritual God, Our Father, and in the immortal saints who are in the heaven beyond earth. This is according to revelations of theological, mystical dogma. We know there are universal and eternal truths that always were and always will be. We know such truths cause us to be pessimistic, reactionary, negativistic, altruistic, and credulous introverts. We repress and prohibit others to benefit the best, the high-class nobility in God's world, with its inflexible, theistic, autocratic social order and hierarchy. We are self-conscious of our soul which always says 'No.' We are free to do what is not normally prohibited by canon law and the 'Ten Commandments.' These say, 'Thou shalt not' and 'The government shall.' "

The 16th century renaissance intellectual spoke next. He said, "Medieval man is wrong with his superstitious beliefs. Citizens, we live in a self-determined world of Nature where man is born with free will. Man must control himself by self-discipline decided by philosophical reason. These logical, rational, natural, abstract formulations and conceptions are expressed in humanistic terms. They are taught by scholastic, dialectic lectures. They are taught by patriotic professors to questioning disputants in quiet debate at the university. We live by ethical standards and the conscious realization of our conscious mind. These intellectual guides form our formal, controlled, sober, and ethical personality. We conceive of thinkers who dispute on the matter and unity of political persons and theories. We conceive of philosophical, humanistic humanities that teach the living sciences. We inductively reason to maintain deductively integrated knowledge in unified universal wholes."

The strange red character interrupted, "Whew! This abstract stuff is out of my world!"

A burning look from the Wise Judge put him in his place.

The renaissance intellectual continued: "We live classical lives of moderation as we control desires by holiday etiquette and formality. We think, and our reason tells us to believe in the mentality of humanity, in our Fatherland, and in the immortality of mortal scholars who live in the abstract world beyond earth. This is according to conclusions of philosophical, logical syllogisms. We think truth is relative, changing, and subject to logical evaluation. We think such truths cause us to be indifferent, conservative, neutral, idealistic, and skeptical ambiverts. We moderate inhibitions to benefit the average, the middle-class bourgeoisie, in Nature's world, with its flexible, agnostic, republican social order and ranking. We are conscious of our mind which always says 'Maybe.' We are free to do what is ethically discretionary according to canon law, civil law, or the social contract theory. These say, 'You should' and 'The government should not.'"

The third philosopher, the 20th century modern scientist then spoke. "Superstitious medieval man is wrong, and so is renaissance man with his old-fashioned generalities. Comrades, we live in a world of man where man is born good. Man must be uncontrolled and undisciplined according to scientific experimenters. Their experimental, sensory, unnatural, materialistic inventions and perceptions are expressed by mechanistic mathematics. These are taught by scientific, pedantic discussions led by individualistic chairmen to participating instigators, in the noisy investigation of the laboratory. We live by legal law and the past subconscious experience of our bodies. Sensory guides deform and make our informal, relaxed, gay, social popularity. We perceive by psychological, mechanistic, materialistic sciences, or by the non-living sciences. We inductively experiment to disintegrate knowledge into specialized parts. We live ornate lives of excess as we exhibit desires at vacation banquets and parties."

The character gave a satanic chuckle and said, "That is the kind of sinful man I like."

"You can go to hell," said the Wise Judge, "if you will not be quiet."

The modern scientist continued: "We see that experience proves man's sensuality and animal nature, and also that our fathers were mortal and are buried in the dirt of the earth. This is according to proof of scientific, experimental statistics. We see that truth is relative, changing, temporal, and subject to further statistical survey. We act on these truths to become optimistic, radical, positivistic, realistic, and cynical extroverts. We stress exhibition in order to benefit the mass, the low-class proletariat, in man's world, with its dynamic, atheistic, democratic social classes and equality. We are unconscious of all but the body which always says 'Yes.' We are free to do what is legally mandatory according to civil law and the 'Bill of Rights.' These say 'You can' and 'The government cannot.' "

The Wise Judge then spoke: "What is truth? Medieval man claimed truth until renaissance man said he was wrong. Renaissance man claimed truth until modern man said both were wrong. Now modern man claims truth; will future man say he is wrong? What is truth when medieval spiritual truth is displaced by renaissance intellectual truth

which is displaced by modern sensory truth? Is there more
to a day than darkness, twilight, and daylight? Twilight follows daylight; what follows twilight? Is there more to truth
than the spiritual, intellectual, and the sensual? Is there
more to truth than the negative, neutral, and positive? If
not, then modern man's sensory truth will be followed by
what?"

The strange creature from the world of darkness was
about to say something to the humans from the twilight of
earth when the Wise Judge from the world of light made
him dumb.

The Wise Judge continued, "Which is the more valu-
able part of the day, darkness, twilight, or daylight? Which
part is not needed to make truth? What is truth? You all
speak profound truths, yet you all contradict each other.
Maybe a greater truth is had if we integrate conflicting
truths into a unified truth? Maybe truth is a trinity of negative, neutral, and positive values? To quote proverbial wisdom: 'Times change; truths change with them. All things
change, yet nothing perishes.' Now before you three opposing philosophers can enter into the inner sanctum of the
wise, I leave this riddle of the trinity of truth for you to
solve from the clues I have given you."

The three philosophers then went off to rack their brains
to solve this riddle of the trinity of truth—the riddle of
three truths in one. Placing their three heads together they
began to integrate their three different philosophies into
one.

They all agreed that the abstract nature of a unified philosophy could best be expressed by key words and symbols. They reasoned out the basis of their philosophy in this
manner: A trinity is symbolized by either a balance scale or
a triangle. By placing their three different philosophies on
either of these symbols according to their historical sequence, they would have three changing philosophies in an
unchanging trinity. By integrating the balance scale and the

triangle they agreed on a unified symbol to express their unified philosophy, thus:

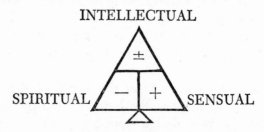

Unified Balancing Trinity

The three philosophers agreed that medieval man tended to be more spiritual in nature than renaissance or modern man. Also, renaissance man tended to be intellectual, and modern man tends to be sensual relative to the other two. Because the spiritual and sensual were poles apart the philosophers arbitrarily called the SPIRITUAL a NEGATIVE value and the SENSUAL a POSITIVE value. Between the opposing POSITIVE and NEGATIVE values was the INTELLECTUAL or NEUTRAL value. (From this point on trinities of three related values will be capitalized.)

Like a see-saw, any change on this balance scale in one value causes a balancing change in the other values to maintain an unchanging entity. Thus as SENSUAL values increase, in balance, SPIRITUAL and INTELLECTUAL values decrease.

Verifying the truth of this unitary principle, of this cyclical balance, or of this trinity of truth, the three philosophers applied the principle to the different NEGATIVE, NEUTRAL, and POSITIVE values of their MEDIEVAL, RENAISSANCE, and MODERN philosophies. Each wrote out his philosophy and capitalized specific values, thus:

MEDIEVAL man: "SIR, We live in a PREDETERMINED WORLD OF GOD where MAN IS BORN EVIL.

Man must be CONTROLLED by DISCIPLINES set by RELIGIOUS AUTHORITY . . ."

RENAISSANCE man: "CITIZENS, We live in a SELF-DETERMINED WORLD OF NATURE where MAN IS BORN WITH FREE WILL. Man must SELF-CONTROL himself by SELF-DISCIPLINE decided by his PHILO-SOPHICAL REASON . . ."

MODERN man: "COMRADES, We live in a WORLD OF MAN where MAN IS BORN GOOD. Man must be UNCONTROLLED and UNDISCIPLINED according to SCIENTIFIC EXPERIENCE . . ."

They then listed these capitalized values thus:

Spiritual *Negative Values*	*Intellectual* *Neutral Values*	*Sensual* *Positive Values*
Sir	Citizen	Comrade
Predetermined	Self-determined	Determined
World of God	World of Nature	World of man
Man born evil	Man born free will	Man born good
Controlled	Self-controlled	Uncontrolled
Disciplined	Self-disciplined	Undiscplined
Religious	Philosophical	Scientific
Authority	Reason	Experience
Etc.	Etc.	Etc.

They did this to all the values mentioned in their original report to the Wise Judge, in the order they were mentioned, and composed this list:

12th C. Medieval Spiritual *Negative Values*	16th C. Renaissance Intellectual *Neutral Values*	20th C. Modern Sensual *Positive Values*

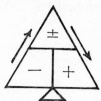

Intuitive	Logical	Experimental
Supersensory	Rational	Sensory
Supernatural	Natural	Unnatural

Divine	Abstract	Material
Creation	Formulation	Invention
Revelation	Conception	Perception
Mystic	Humanistic	Mechanistic
Symbols	Words	Numbers
Spiritualistic	Scholastic	Scientific
Rhetoric	Dialectic	Pedantic

(See appendix for completion of this list.)

They realized that thousands of these changing, unified NEGATIVE, NEUTRAL, and POSITIVE values could be listed to indicate the unified whole of the unchanging eternal and universal trinity of truth. For all values are either NEGATIVE, NEUTRAL, or POSITIVE with degrees of these between. They had found the roots of the tree of knowledge and a source of wisdom.

They realized that the key words that composed these balanced trinities referred to extreme NEGATIVE, NEUTRAL, and POSITIVE degrees. So they pointed out that the degrees of difference between these extremes vary just as they do between the intellectual extremes of the IDIOT, AVERAGE, and GENIUS. But if need be they could indicate smaller degrees of difference, thus: The MYSTIC-HUMANISTIC-SCIENTIFIC balance can be subdivided to, MYSTIC — Scholastic — HUMANISTIC — Relativistic — Skeptic — SCIENTIFIC — Cynic — Nihilistic — return to MYSTIC.

The three philosophers realized truth was an unchanging trinity of changing NEGATIVE, NEUTRAL, and POSITIVE values. They symbolized their unified philosophy thus:

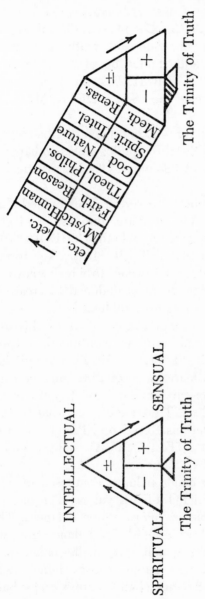

The Trinity of Truth

How diverse balances parallel each other and integrate to a unified whole.

INTELLECTUAL

SENSUAL

SPIRITUAL

The Trinity of Truth

How changing NEGATIVE, NEUTRAL, and POSITIVE values are unified in an unchanging trinity.

The Unity of Diversity

This symbolized trinity enabled the philosophers to state a unified principle: Constant balancing cyclical change of NEGATIVE, NEUTRAL, and POSITIVE values, within an unchanging entity or trinity of truth, is a unifying law of God, Nature, and should be of Man. Such laws, they agreed, are PREDETERMINED, but their degree of DETERMINATION can be SELF-DETERMINED by man.

The skeptical character who had been silent so long now joined in when he saw the three philosophers so happy over their new theory. He said, "So what! Of what practical value is this system?"

One of the philosophers answered, "This unified philosophy is a basis for finding ultimate, universal and eternal truths in all fields of knowledge, whether THEOLOGICAL, PHILOSOPHICAL, or SCIENTIFIC. It is a key to unlock the sources of knowledge. It is a key to which known facts can be induced or unknown facts deduced to create ideas and simplify the most complex problems."

To further explain the practical values of this unified principle system the philosopher continued: "Knowing nothing of PAST, PRESENT, or FUTURE individuals, families, groups, cities, nations, or civilizations, we can follow their general historical sequence and pattern by referring to these balance lists. Thus we can say that the Greek and the Roman civilizations ROSE on SPIRITUAL values, reached a PEAK on INTELLECTUAL values, and DECLINED on MATERIAL values.

"A civilization is a major balance composed of NEGATIVE, NEUTRAL, and POSITIVE values. The major balance is a unified whole of many minor balances. This is symbolized by a mobile composed of a balance from which suspend smaller balances, which have smaller balances.

"Every major balance change causes minor balance changes. Every minor balance change causes major balance changes to maintain a balance within the whole entity. As the overall civilization balance changes, thousands of political, social, economic, moral, and psychological balances have paralleling changes.

"Social balance changes involve conflict as unchanging REACTONARIES resist changing RADICALS. Between these are CONSERVATIVES who decide which side of the balance they will place their weight to cause or resist change. In the 14th century there was conflict between pope and council, church and state, scholastic and humanist, nobility and burgher, etc. These opposing REACTIONARY and RADICAL (RADICAL relative to the PAST; CONSERVATIVE relative to the FUTURE) social forces had values which parallel the NEGATIVE and NEUTRAL column of the balance list. The victorious RADICALS with values in the NEUTRAL column then went on to become REACTIONARY forces to oppose rising RADICALS with values in the POSITIVE column.

"Knowing one side of a balance scale we can deduce unknown values on the other side. Knowing man stresses SPIRITUAL values on civilization's RISE we can deduce that he stresses its opposite on civilization's DECLINE, i.e., MATERIAL values.

"Such a unified balance list indicates what forces conflicted in the PAST, are conflicting in the PRESENT, and will conflict in the FUTURE—thus RELIGIOUS wars on the RISE, PATRIOTIC wars at the PEAK, and ECONOMIC wars on DECLINE. Knowing such a unified balance system enables predictions, based on PAST experiences, which permit self-disciplined preparation in the PRESENT to control the FUTURE."

The red-faced listener was lost in a cloud of abstractions, but the philosopher went on:

"Such a universal structure of historical balances enables one to know what civilization phase he is in. It enables him to know that when his civilization, and also himself, and his family, group, and nation, are described only by POSITIVE column terms, then he had better regain self-disciplined moderation to maintain his gains.

"This unified balance system enables one to place a historical fact in its proper perspective rather than accepting it as belonging to history in general. Thus in reading that the Romans were great political administrators and engineers we can reject it because it does not apply to all of Rome's thousand year cycle of history. Rather we can assume that paralleling the SPIRITUALISTIC—HUMANISTIC—SCIENTIFIC balance the Romans were great political administrators during their MIDDLE or HUMANISTIC age, and great engineers during their LATTER or SCIENTIFIC age. The same principle is true of 'Greek democracy' which applies only to the HUMANISTIC, INTELLECTUAL, or NEUTRAL phase of their balancing cycle of history."

The uninvited character was still trying to comprehend what he had heard five minutes previously, but still the philosopher went on:

"It is natural to combine different words from the NEGATIVE column to get a meaningful sentence. Thus, 'INTROVERTS are INHIBITED, SILENT, MORBID CHARACTERS who prefer to LISTEN and MEDITATE.' Or from the NEUTRAL column: 'AMBIVERTS are CONTROLLED, QUIET, SOBER PERSONALITIES who prefer to TEACH and DEBATE.' Or from the POSITIVE column: 'EXTROVERTS are EXHIBITING, NOISY, GAY, POPULAR persons who prefer to LEAD and ACTIVATE.'

"But attempt to combine NEGATIVE, NEUTRAL, and POSITIVE values into a meaningful sentence and our mind cannot resolve the conflict of ideas—it goes blank. If we insist on decoding such an eclectic mess, we get a headache. Thus: 'The INTROVERT is an EXHIBITING, GAY, SOBER PERSONALITY who prefers to MEDITATE and ACTIVATE.' Such an eclectic stew of values is popular in declining material societies as mechanical imitation and quantity replace intellectual creation and quality. At such times eclectic phrases like 'INTELLECTUAL SCIENTIFIC RELIGION, REACTIONARY CONSERVATIVE RADICALS, AND PATRIOTIC INDIVIDUALISTIC INTERNATIONALISTS,' cause mass mental blanks and the disintegration of human thinking processes. This destroys mental REVELATION, CONCEPTION, and PERCEPTION, to enable the final social disintegration and material destruction of a SPIRITUALLY dead, MENTALLY senile, and PHYSICALLY weak race."

The philosopher ran out of breath and another continued thus:

"The psychologist can generally describe an introvert's personality once he has any indication of the introvert pattern. On the same principle, if we know anything at all about a person, we can, from this starting point, deduce his general personality, goals, beliefs, etc., by applying this unified balance list. Thus to describe personalities (Using only words from this work's balance list):

Introvert	Ambivert	Extrovert
Listener	Teacher	Leader
Morbid	Sober	Gay
Strive for character	Strive for personality	Strive for popularity
Meditator	Debater	Activater
Inhibited	Controlled	Exhibited
Silent	Quiet	Noisy
etc.	etc.	etc.

"On this principle, knowing nothing of medieval thought, gothic art, mystic philosophy, reactionary minds, the beginnings of a civilization, or any other form of knowledge in this category, we can learn of them by going down the NEGATIVE column to select and associate related key words.

"Or knowing nothing of modern art, mechanistic philosophy, radical minds, or extrovert personalities, we can learn of them by going down the list of POSITIVE key words.

"The same principle applies to any political, social, economic, moral, psychological, or educational movement. If we desire to know about changing philosophies, educational goals, social customs, political beliefs, or changing national history, or if we seek the true meaning of words, then we follow the key words as they change from NEGATIVE to NEUTRAL to POSITIVE value, thus:

Words to define meanings:

Spiritual Words	Intellectual Words	Materialistic Words
Soul	Mind	Body
Mystic	Humanistic	Mechanistic
Theologic	Philosophic	Scientific
Altruistic	Idealistic	Realistic
Faith	Reason	Experience

To explain what different fields of knowledge involve:

Theology	Philosophy	Science
Soul	Mind	Body
Mystic	Humanistic	Mechanistic
Spiritual	Intellectual	Material
God	Nature	Man
Divinities	Humanities	Sciences

To explain changing educational goals by what is stressed:

Medieval	Renaissance	Modern
Spiritual	Intellectual	Sensual
Meaning	Matter	Method
Disciplined	Self-disciplined	Undisciplined
Divinities	Humanities	Sciences
Moral	Ethical	Social

To explain changing art (painting, sculpture, music, etc.) by its description:

Medieval (Gothic)	Renaissance (Classic)	Modern (Impressionist)
Spiritual theme	Intellectual	Sensual
Symbols	Ideas	Things
Altruistic	Idealistic	Realistic
God's world	Nature's world	Man's world
Theological	Philosophical	Psychological

To distinguish and describe political beliefs and followers:

Reactionary	Conservative	Radical
Autocratic	Republican	Democratic
Pessimistic	Indifferent	Optimistic
Negative	Neutral	Positive
Against change	Maybe change	For change
Moral	Ethical	Legal .

By this time the strange listener realized that he was not a philosopher and went back down below to shovel in more coal before the fires went out. The philosophers continued talking to the Wise Judge.

"Hundreds of different elements of knowledge can be explained by using similar values in their unified balanced order. Thus this is a system of unified principles that is a source of knowledge and wisdom."

The three philosophers who started all this now thought they had solved the riddle of the trinity of truth. They realized that each spoke the truth, or at least a relative changing truth that was part of a greater unchanging truth. They realized that all three values—NEGATIVE, NEUTRAL, and POSITIVE—were needed to benefit a MANKIND, HUMANITY, and MAN composed of the BEST, the AVERAGE, and the WORST, of IDIOTS, AVERAGE MINDS, and GENIUSES. Only in excessive extremes were these values evil. Just as dark shadows are needed to contrast with light to make the harmonious, balanced unity of a painting, so NEGATIVE values are needed to balance the POSITIVE to give a unified meaning. Opposing values have a NEUTRAL value between. Excessive sun brings drought; excessive rain brings flood. Between these extremes is a point of dynamic moderation that gives constant balancing cyclical change of sun and rain.

Having solved the riddle of the trinity of truth the three philosophers relaxed contented among the MEDITATING, CONTEMPLATING, and EXPERIMENTING wise men in that ivory tower in the clouds—in the inner sanctum of the wise.

Thus:

Truth is a trinity of NEGATIVE, NEUTRAL, and POSITIVE values.

Civilizations RISE with NEGATIVE SPIRITUAL values; Peak with NEUTRAL INTELLECTUAL values; and DECLINE with POSITIVE SENSORY values.

Progressive, constant balancing cyclical change of NEGATIVE, NEUTRAL, and POSITIVE values within an unchanging entity, is a unified law of GOD, NATURE, and MAN.

Appendix

Unified Balance List (From the cycle of Western Civilization)

12th C. Medieval Spiritual values Negative values	16th C. Renaissance Intellectual values Neutral values	20th C. Modern Sensual values Positive values
sermon	lecture	discussion
preach	teach	lead
pious	patriotic	individualistic
priest	professor	chairman
listen	question	participate
meditation	disputation	investigation
silent	quiet	noisy
meditate	debate	instigate
monastery	university	laboratory
moral	ethical	legal
code	standard	law
conscience	conscious	subconscious
soul	mind	body
spiritual	intellectual	sensual
forming	formed	deforming
unformed	formal	informal
stern	controlled	relaxed
morbid	sober	gay
moral	ethical	social
character	personality	popularity

believe	conceive	perceive
know	think	do
meditation	disputation	activation
meaning	matter	method
ideas	persons	things
doctrine	theory	practice
theological	philosophical	psychological
spiritualistic	humanistic	mechanistic
divinities	humanities	sciences
anti-science	"living sciences"	"dead sciences"
deductive	deductive-inductive	inductive
integrate	integrated	disintegrate
universal	humanistic	individualistic
simple	classic	ornate
deficiency	moderation	excess
inhibit	control	exhibit
holy day	holiday	vacation day
believe	think	see
faith	reason	experience
spiritual	mental	sensual
God	man	animal
"Our Father"	"Fatherland"	parent
immortals	mortal-immortals	mortals
saints	scholars	scientists
theologic	philosophic	scientific
mystical	logical	experimental
dogmatic	syllogistic	statistic
pessimistic	indifferent	optimistic
reactionary	conservative	radical
altruistic	idealistic	realistic
introvert	ambivert	extrovert
credulous	skeptical	cynical
self-conscious	conscious	unconscious
soul	mind	body
no	maybe	yes
prohibit	inhibit	exhibit
for best	for average	for worst
high-class	middle-class	low-class
nobility	bourgeoisie	proletariat
God's world	Nature's world	Man's world
theistic	agnostic	atheistic
autocratic	republican	democratic
moral	ethical	legal
prohibitory	discretionary	mandatory
"Thou shalt not"	You may	You can
"Ten Commandments"	"Social Contract"	"Bill of Rights"

KEYS TO THE SOURCES OF KNOWLEDGE

(On symbolically associating unified principles)

"A goal of learning," said the lecturing professor, "is to obtain universal and eternal principles that entail the broadest area of knowledge possible. In this age of specialization there is a critical need for these basic principles to unify diverse fields of knowledge."

He further explained how principles were derived. After the lecture a student approached the professor and said, "Let me repeat you," he said. "By combining brothers, sisters, and parents, we get a broader idea called a family. Integrate families and we get a broader concept called a nation. Unite nations and we have a broader principle called a civilization. The principle of a civilization entails all social organizations. This principle then is a source of all social knowledge. Is this correct?"

"I would say so," said the curious professor, "why do you ask?"

"Because if that is so," said the bright student, "then by compiling all such principles would we have the basis of all knowledge?"

"I have never heard this thesis before," the scholarly professor said, "but I suppose we would." Then in the wonderment of insight he added, "But how could anyone acquire and organize such a mass of information?"

"I think it can be done," said the persistent youth, "let me explain. You said the word 'civilization' symbolizes a principle. This principle is the peak of a hierarchy of millions of social facts and concepts. If this be true, then cannot we extend this hierarchy to its ultimate conclusion? If we can unite facts into concepts and concepts into principles, why cannot we unite principles into broader major principles? Would not these major principles entail and be the basis of all principles, concepts, and facts below it? Would not these be a basis of all knowledge and wisdom?"

The wise professor was amazed at the unfolding revelations and said in the subdued tones of the awed, "Yes, they would be keys to the source of knowledge."

Then subconscious fears welled up in the wise old man's heart and mind. The idea that this youth could reveal such wisdom to him, when he should be revealing wisdom to the youth, made him tighten up in defense. With professorial authority and professional resistance he said, "It would take years to collect these principles, years to compile them, and hundreds of volumes to record them. So I suppose time and cost make this project impossible."

This discouraging note failed to discourage the eager student. "Well," he said, "suppose we collected a random sample of these principles and sorted them into different piles. Each pile would contain principles having a common element. Each pile would be identified by a key word. Now could not all the principles collected be condensed to a fewer number of major principles? Could not each major principle be a more basic source of knowledge?"

The wise professor succeeded in applying his own wisdom to control his emotional resistance. Instead of fighting his student's ideas he wanted to help him. "Yes," he said, "you would be closer to the ultimate sources of knowledge, but how could you express such an abstract major principle?"

"That should be no problem," said the increasingly enthusiastic student, "for the answer is already given in expressing narrower principles. Thus the word 'civilization' symbolizes an abstract principle that cannot be seen. To communicate this idea we symbolize it by a word to make the unknown known. On the same principle, to make known and to communicate the abstract idea of a major principle we must symbolize it by a word."

"That seems logical," said the fascinated wise man, "but why not experiment with this theory to see what results?"

The industrious student did just that. Working day and night he collected spiritual wisdom, philosophical principles, mathematical axioms, scientific laws, literary truisms, and age-old proverbs. He put those having a common element in separate piles which he symbolized by a key word. He read books that summarized knowledge and wisdom, underlined their principles, cut these out, and added them to related piles of principles.

He evolved ninety piles of principles which seemed too excessive, too complex, and too confusing. But sparked by a flash of insight he thought, "I have condensed thousands of principles into ninety major principles; maybe there are common elements within this ninety to enable a fewer number of unified principles?"

While synthesizing the ninety major principles into forty unified principles he perceived other common elements which enabled further synthesis into twenty-one unified principles. These were the essence of knowledge and wisdom. The key words symbolizing these unified principles were keys to the sources of knowledge. Each unified principle could apply to all fields of knowledge whether theological, philosophical, or scientific, and to all the progressive ranges of society—the individual, family, group, city, nation, and civilization. Each was like one of the seven basic plots out of which all stories evolve—only the relative facts of time, place, individual, circumstance, and degree made the principle different.

The pioneering student then evaluated synonyms of

these key words to determine which was most practical for everyday communication. From such synonyms as "aim, purpose, objective, intention, destination, and goal," he selected "goal" as a unified principle key word to symbolize the basis of man's spiritual, intellectual, and sensual activity.

Other unified principle key words he determined were:

"Spiritual-intellectual-sensual": Roots from which stem all the branches of the tree of knowledge; the trinity of knowledge.

"Change": A principle in all things spiritual, intellectual, and sensual.

"Balance" and "Cycle": Kinds of change.

"Negative-neutral-positive": Trinity of values within which change takes place.

"Standard": Guide by which positive-negative degrees of change from a neutral basis are perceived and evaluated.

"Moderation": Controls change.

"Self-discipline": Key to human control of change.

"Cumulate": Increasing momentum and multiplication of uncontrolled change.

"Progressive": Control of change by evolutionary degrees, not revolutionary violence.

"Atrophy": Deterioration due to lack of change.

"Relative": The changing evaluation of truth which is related to time, space, individual, circumstance, and degree.

"Judo": Reaction to change by falling back to regain control.

"Progressive Range": Pyramidic structure of change.

"Self-discipline Cycle": Change in human values from spiritual to intellectual to sensual on the progressive ranges of society—the individual, family, group, city, nation, and civilization.

"Distribution Balance": Balanced distribution of all negative-neutral-positive elements in nature.

"Perspective Perception": The relative nature of perception in time and space.

"Association": Key to intellectual activities; how one idea relates to another in a cumulative chain of ideas.

"Trinity": Synthesis of negative-neutral-positive elements of knowledge into a unified trinity of three-in-one.

"Direct Achievement": Key to achieving man's spiritual, intellectual, and sensual goals.

Of course this list of unified principle key words was not the ultimate in knowledge and wisdom, no moie so than the first airplane was the ultimate in aeronautical knowledge. But it was a crude framework upon which others could build.

The wise young scholar contacted the wise old scholar and said, "I believe I have found the keys to the sources of knowledge—the unified principles that sum up all principles."

"This is an amazing achievement," said the open-minded but skeptical professor, "but what value is this knowledge without use or benefit?"

"I thought of that," quickly answered the wise theorist, "and I may have some answers. First, you may be skeptical that all knowledge and wisdom can be derived from only a few unified principles. But this is similar to having all words based on only twenty-six letters of the alphabet. A few math principles are the basis of all mathematical knowledge. About one hundred atomic elements are the basis of all material things. So, on the same principle, a few unified principles are the basis of all knowledge.

"Would there be knowledge without the communication the twenty-six letters of the alphabet enable? Cannot combinations of a few math principles solve all math problems, no matter how complex? What chemical knowledge would there be without the hundred chemicals which are symbolized on the periodic table of chemical elements?

"What twenty-six alphabet letters do for symbolizing and communicating ideas, twenty-one unified principle key words can also do. What a few math principles can do for solving all math problems, a few unified principles can do for solving all life problems. What the symbols on the periodic table of atomic elements do for chemical knowledge, the symbols for unified principles can do for all knowledge."

"I can see," said the learning wise man, "how whole fields of knowledge are based on and benefited by only a few principles. It seems logical the same can apply to unified principles relative to all knowledge. But are these the only value of unified principles?"

"No," said the brilliant boy, "another value is in improving the thinking processes of man. A goal of formal education is to develop maximum use of mental capabilities and abilities. Any use of intelligence involves thinking. All thinking is either relating facts to a principle or deducing facts from a principle. If the mind has no principle to associate facts, there can be no thinking. On the other hand, the more principles in the mind the more facts can be associated, and the greater will be the capacity and ability to think.

"Unified principles also prepare one to perceive facts he would not ordinarily perceive. They enable one to perceive facts related to a principle, and to reject unrelated facts that confuse thinking. Also, whenever a new fact is integrated with an old principle a new idea is created, just as one plus two equals three. So unified principles can be a step to advance man's mind by improving his thinking and creative abilities."

"This sounds interesting, even if a bit radical," said the conservative wise man. "These benefits alone make it worthwhile, but it seems you still have more to say."

"Yes," said the excited youth who was just waiting for

an opening to continue, "the benefits of unified principles are unlimited but here is another important one. We cannot learn the new or the unknown without associating it to the old or the known. Unified principles, as the basis of all knowledge, are knowns by which to associate and learn the unknown. Thus unified principles can enable one to learn much more rapidly and thoroughly."

"We can certainly use that in this age of ever-increasing knowledge," said the reflecting wise man.

"But that is not all," said the youth who was just getting warm in his exposition. "A key number enables one to find a forgotten fact in a library of billions of facts. On this principle, unified principle key words enable one to find forgotten facts in the storehouse of forgotten facts—the subconscious mind. Mention the word 'civilization' to a historian and he has a broad perspective of meaning. To an ignorant child it means nothing. Mention a unified principle key word to an understander and it is like a picture worth a thousand words in recalling and associating forgotten facts. To one ignorant of unified principles it means nothing."

"This is amazing," said the truly amazed professor.

The enthusiastic youth needed no encouragement to go on. "Millions of facts are classified in an encyclopedia under key words. On the same principle, millions of facts can be classified under a few unified principle key words. To find an answer to problems without unified principle key words is like finding a fact in an encyclopedia without using alphabetical key words."

"You have convinced me," said the profoundly affected man, "but I believe your truths will not effect others as they have affected me, regardless of their benefit to individual man and to mankind in general. Man fears what he does not know, and will resist your unknown unified principles until they become generally known. Four hundred years ago Gallileo discovered a telescope and a new concept of the universe. Scholars and authorities refused to look into his telescope which would have proven his concept. Instead they persecuted him and forced him to deny his truths. They feared facing a truth which would disprove the knowledge that made them scholars and authorities. This can happen to you. You have a long life ahead of you, young man, and I would not like to see you suffer by a mankind for whom you now sacrifice time and effort to enlighten. Maybe your truths will be accepted fifty years from now. Meanwhile, I hope you will not be like other inventors and creators. They spent their lives in poverty and died in it while creating and developing their ideas, only to have the rich capitalize on their idea for profit and for fame as its creator. And as others seek what you have already found, expect others to claim your idea."

The youth meditated a moment and said, "If we can unify principles to get unified principles, then the ultimate conclusion is that we can unify unified principles to get a unitary principle—the final principle that is ultimately behind all knowledge, whether spiritual, intellectual, or sensual. Maybe this ultimate unitary principle is a trinity of three. How else can negative-neutral-positive values be unified? This is an idea often expressed by ancient mystics and by many today who believe in a Source of All Things which is a Trinity of three-in-one. Therefore my unified principle theory which leads to this Unitary Principle doctrine cannot be so new. The more I think of my new idea the more humbled I become in realizing I have only reasoned logically what others had revealed mystically and what others will prove scientifically."

The wise old man stood silently in humble respect.

The wise young youth stood silently in humble respect of the wise old man. It was difficult to write such truths but more difficult for an old scholar to see and admit truth from a young student. He was truly a wise man who could admit ignorance in order to admit more wisdom.

Thus:

Perfume is the essence of thousands of flowers; a unified principle is the essence of millions of facts.

Concepts sum facts; principles sum concepts; unified principles sum principles.

Millions of facts unify to thousands of concepts, which unify to hundreds of principles, which unify to a few unified principles, which unify in a Unitary Principle.

WISDOM IS ONE

(On the symbolic manifestation of unified principles)

A wise king desired to pass the lessons of his hard-earned experience on to his son and heir. But that common destiny, death, approached sooner than expected. He could never teach his young son all he knew.

To teach his son after he was gone he summoned the greatest scholars in the kingdom.

A physicist, psychologist, sociologist, anthropologist, political-scientist, philosopher, and a theologist arrived. Each brought carloads of books, books to explain these books, books to clarify these books, and more books to index these books about books.

The king took one look at this vast library of knowledge and exasperatingly exiled them back to their campuses. But not until he exclaimed, "One of you could never teach my son all you know, let alone all of you. He would die of old age before one of you finished. Apparently, wisdom is what I seek, not knowledge."

Unhappily he prepared to die as a king should—happily.

Sitting dejectedly on his throne he observed his courtiers scheming to dominate his naive, ignorant son. They already manifested contempt for him by their loud laughter. One joking jester remarked sarcastically, "Everyone else has tried, maybe the old, hairless hermit on the river can teach his son. He has an answer for every problem—but so does the fortune teller at the teahouse. Ha! Ha!"

The bitter king decided to return these flaunting taunters back to their haunts. He summoned the learned hermit to his court. He would show these sycophantic sinecurists how he trusted a stranger more than them.

When the humble hermit arrived, the mighty king asked softly, "Can you teach my son what I have learned?"

"I cannot teach him all the facts learned in your full life, Sire," answered the hermit, "but maybe I can teach him the wisdom gleaned from your millions of facts. Maybe I can teach principles to guide him through the maze of facts acquired in his own life."

"But where are the books you will require?" queried the skeptical king.

"Books are not required to teach wisdom," replied the hermit whose head was his library.

The surprised king exclaimed, "Are you saying a lifetime of wisdom can be taught in less than one volume! Impossible!"

"Yes, Sire," answered the humorless hermit. "Your son can solve millions of mathematical problems by learning a few basic mathematical principles. Likewise, he can solve millions of life's problems by learning a few unified principles."

"You will have the opportunity to prove your claim," said the interested king. "You will summarize my wisdom in less than one volume."

In a matter of fact tone the hermit added, "I will do it in one chapter, Sire."

The king, with the confused look of one not knowing whether he dealt with idiot or genius, dismissed the hermit.

The following day the hermit returned to present his report to the king. The king skimmed the pages and per-

ceived that the Introduction was almost as long as the
report itself. Also, the report was written in an unusual
manner, the likes of which he had never seen. Shrugging,
as one does when he is willing to try something he is skeptical of, he went to his chambers to read it.

Later he told the honored hermit, "I read your report
several times. It was difficult reading, but each reading
became incredibly more easy. I read it several times before
grasping its profound significance. But again, each reading
reaped rich, rewarding wisdom not had before. You have
truly summarized the wisdom I desire in my son."

The king died happily knowing his son would rule
wisely ever after under the guidance of his principles.

The consternated, conniving courtiers contentedly continued as simple sycophantic sinecurists when they realized the wisdom of the son.

The hermit's wish was granted—he was left alone to
contemplate universal problems while being an informal
adviser to the king.

What did the king read? Fortunately, the king's son
treasured the hermit's report more than gold itself and
had preserved it well. After his death the report was made
public. Here it is:

Introduction

Millions of facts UNIFY to thousands of concepts, which
UNIFY to hundreds of PRINCIPLES, which UNIFY to a
few UNIFIED PRINCIPLES, which UNIFY to an ULTI-
MATE PRINCIPLE.

PRINCIPLES without MANIFESTATION do not exist.
SYMBOLS can MANIFEST the UNPERCEIVED and unknown to make them PERCEIVED and known. This work
is based on UNIFIED PRINCIPLES that are SYMBO-
LIZED by key words and drawings.

The *individual* PERCEIVES what he is PREPARED to PERCEIVE. So these UNIFIED PRINCIPLE key words are capitalized, italicized, and hyphenated to PREPARE their PERCEPTION.

Each key word PRINCIPLE PREPARES the *individual* to PERCEIVE ASSOCIATED concepts and their ASSOCIATED facts—like the word "home" ASSOCIATES *family* scenes.

The PRINCIPLE, SYMBOLIZED by a key word, INTEGRATES with facts in a sentence to synthesize new ideas.

Where the word *individual* is italicized, the words *family, group, city, nation,* and *civilization,* can be EXCHANGED for it in the sentence. For what applies in PRINCIPLE to the *individual* applies in PRINCIPLE to other RANGES of society. For example, "The *individual* (or *family, group, city, nation,* or *civilization*) needs a GOAL."

EXCHANGING these names, in EFFECT, would create six books in one. Each book would be based on a different RANGE of knowledge: psychology, sociology, anthropology, political-science, history, and philosophy. This MANIFESTS "the source of knowledge" nature of UNIFIED PRINCIPLES.

A *SELF-DISCIPLINE* CYCLE is MANIFESTED by the following CYCLICAL DEGREES or RANGES: *survival — hardship — SELF-DISCIPLINE — effort — success — leisure — pleasure — dissipation — degradation — ruin —* and back to *survival.*

These DEGREE words are italicized in sentences to MANIFEST the RELATIONSHIP of all knowledge to the *SELF-DISCIPLINE* CYCLE. If all sentences containing these words were compiled, there would be a book on the *SELF-DISCIPLINE* CYCLE, or ten books on its CYCLICAL DEGREES.

All values are a DEGREE or RANGE between POSI-
TIVE-NEGATIVE LIMITS. This PRINCIPLE is MANI-
FESTED in this work by hyphens that UNITE opposing
but BALANCING ENTITIES and by the symbols $(+)$
$(\pm)$ $(-)$. For example, the following qualities and TRINI-
TIES are hyphenated: broad-narrow RANGES, POSITIVE-
NEGATIVE LIMITS, spiritual-intellectual-sensual knowl-
edge, NEGATIVE-NEUTRAL-POSITIVE values, etc.

Here is a MANIFESTATION of the INTEGRATED
application of capitalized, italicized, and hyphenated words:

From this one sentence, "The *individual* needs *leisure*
for spiritual-intellectual-sensual BALANCE and to create
ideas;" the following and more can be ASSOCIATED by
UNIFIED PRINCIPLE key words:

The key word *"individual"* ASSOCIATES the PRO-
GRESSIVE RANGES of society. This MANIFESTS that
not only the *individual*, but also the *family, group, city,
nation,* and *civilization* need *leisure* to CONTROL BAL-
ANCES and to create ideas.

"Leisure" ASSOCIATES the *SELF-DISCIPLINE* CY-
CYE. The *leisure* DEGREE of the *SELF-DISCIPLINE*
CYCLE is the golden age of creative ideas. It is the peak of
MODERATION$(\pm)$ between deficiency-excess, or between
spiritual-intellectual-sensual values.

SELF-DISCIPLINED effort ACHIEVES the *success*
which enables *leisure*. But excessive *leisure* CUMULATES
to *pleasure* and *dissipation* which *degrades* to *ruin* and
survival hardship. So *leisure* may have POSITIVE-NEGA-
TIVE value RELATIVE to the *individual's* PERSPECTIVE
of it.

The POSITIVE-NEGATIVE values of *leisure* MANI-
FESTS that *SELF-DISCIPLINED* MODERATION$(\pm)$ at
the peak$(\pm)$ of *leisure*$(\pm)$, or between the DEGREES of
effort—dissipation is a STANDARD to CONTROL the
individual and his PROGRESSIVE RANGES of society.

This MANIFESTS a BALANCE between any three PROGRESSIVE DEGREES of the *SELF-DISCIPLINE* CYCLE, i.e., *success*($\pm$) BALANCES between *effort-leisure*. As one value increases($+$) there is a BALANCING decrease($-$) in the others.

The POSITIVE values of *"leisure"* ASSOCIATE as a GOAL to be ACHIEVED. Without *leisure* the *individual* does what he must, not what he wants. The *individual* strives for physical GOALS, then mental, and then spiritual GOALS. Then he reverses this order to complete a CYCLE, unless MODERATED by *SELF-DISCIPLINED effort*. Only *leisure* enables the ACHIEVEMENT and CONTROL of a BALANCED DISTRIBUTION of spiritual-intellectual-sensual GOALS.

More ideas from this sample sentence can be CUMULATED by ASSOCIATION. But these are sufficient to MANIFEST the almost UNLIMITED wisdom and knowledge behind UNIFIED PRINCIPLE key words. Once UNIFIED PRINCIPLES are grasped all knowledge, whether believed-reasoned-PERCEIVED, will ASSOCIATE key words.

The *individual* cannot learn the unknown without a known to ASSOCIATE it. UNIFIED PRINCIPLE key words and SYMBOLS are knowns to ASSOCIATE the unknown. Their POSITIVE EFFECTS on education and learning will be manifold and CUMULATIVE.

Logical reasoning is either inductive (facts to PRINCIPLE) or deductive (PRINCIPLE to facts). UNIFIED PRINCIPLE key words are keys to CONTROL the emotion-reason BALANCE and the inductive-deductive BALANCE of the conscious mind. They SYMBOLIZE PRINCIPLES from which all facts are logically induced-deduced, to ACHIEVE the broadest-narrowest PERSPECTIVE of the fact-PRINCIPLE BALANCE.

UNIFIED PRINCIPLE key words are also keys to AS-

SOCIATE the vast "forgotten" knowledge of the subconscious mind, and keys to CONTROLLING the *individual's* spirit-mind-body BALANCE.

In effect, UNIFIED PRINCIPLES tend to be keys to the sources of all knowledge and wisdom.

UNIFIED Wisdom

Wisdom is a synthesis($\pm$) of thesis-antithesis. Truth is a UNITY of diversity. All knowledge is ONE in the TRINITY of knowledge which is an INTEGRATION of many TRINITIES of knowledge.

God-man-nature are the sources of all spiritual-intellectual-material knowledge which the *individual,* with his moral-mental-sensual nature, believes-reasons-PERCEIVES thru theology-philosophy-science.

TRINITIES have BALANCING NEGATIVE-NEUTRAL-POSITIVE parts. CHANGING part of a TRINITY CAUSES BALANCING CHANGES in other parts to CONTROL and maintain the BALANCED ENTITY. Thus, body EFFECTS mind; mind EFFECTS body, and spirit EFFECTS both in the BALANCE of the *individual* TRINITY.

This BALANCING of the parts that make the whole is MANIFESTED in equations common to natural sciences. But the same PRINCIPLE applies to spiritual-intellectual-scientific knowledge. This is SYMBOLIZED:

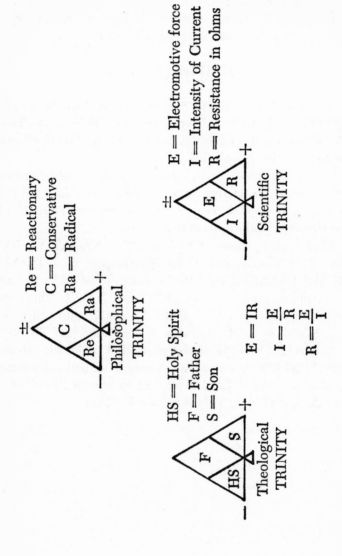

Constant BALANCING CYCLICAL CHANGE of a
NEUTRAL DEGREE between NEGATIVE-POSITIVE
LIMITS to CONTROL an ENTITY or TRINITY is a UNI-
FIED PRINCIPLE of God-man-nature. This is SYMBO-
LIZED:

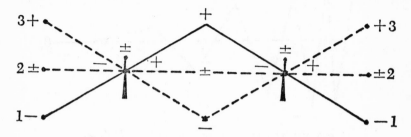

BALANCING CYCLICAL CHANGE

This CYCLICAL BALANCE MANIFESTS that $1^+ +$
$1^- = 0^\pm$; $2^+ + 1^- = 1^+$; $1^+ + 2^- = 1^-$, etc. RELATING
this to human values: $1°$ happiness $+ 2°$ sadness $= 1°$ sadness; $3°$ happiness $- 1°$ sadness $= 2°$ happiness; $1°$ happiness $+ 1°$ sadness $=$ no CHANGE in spirit.

These equations MANIFEST that values cannot be cre-
ated$(+)$ nor destroyed$(-)$, only CHANGED$(\pm)$. One
value cannot increase$(+)$ without a BALANCING de-
crease$(-)$ in the others to maintain the BALANCED EN-
TITY. The parts that make the whole can all increase$(+)$
or decrease$(-)$ only if the whole is increased-decreased.

Values are a CHANGING NEUTRAL DEGREE be-
tween NEGATIVE-POSITIVE LIMITS or RANGES.
Rhythmic harmony of a CYCLICAL BALANCE is
ACHIEVED by CONTROLLING the DEGREE of
CHANGE to MODERATE excess-deficiency.

This is SYMBOLIZED:

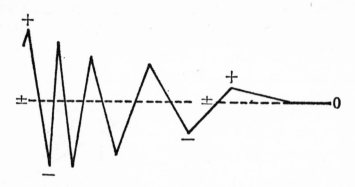

CONTROLLING CYCLICAL BALANCES

For example, ecstasy(+) BALANCES misery(—); happiness BALANCES sadness; contentment BALANCES moodiness; no emotion CAUSES the zombie. Thus the higher the *individual* rises(+) the sooner and further he falls(—).

On the bottom(—), the *individual* can only rise(+) happily(+) with each step; on the top(+), he can only go down(—) unhappily(—) with each step.

As the CYCLICAL peak-depth RANGE increases(+), its time RANGE decreases(—); as the peak-depth RANGE decreases, in BALANCE, its time RANGE increases to maintain the time-space ENTITY BALANCE. The contented may not enjoy ecstasy, but does enjoy his contentment longer and does not suffer the misery that BALANCES ecstasy.

Man-nature have a BALANCED DISTRIBUTION of NEGATIVE-NEUTRAL-POSITIVE values. Thus, idiots(—) BALANCE geniuses(+) while the average(±) in between have the broadest RANGE. From the average(±) as a STANDARD there PROGRESSES POSITIVE-NEGATIVE DEGREES or RANGES of mentality. This is SYMBOLIZED:

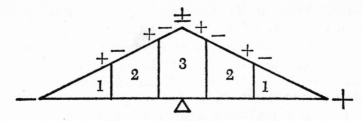

The DISTRIBUTION BALANCE

Values are a RELATIVE DEGREE from a STANDARD of comparison between POSITIVE-NEGATIVE LIMITS or RANGES. Values are RELATIVE to time-space, *individual* and DEGREE. The same value is minor(—) RELATIVE to a major(+) value and, major RELATIVE to a minor value. The same line is long-short RELATIVE to another line. The *individual* is both happy-sad, strong-weak, superior-inferior, etc. RELATIVE to a POSITIVE-NEGATIVE STANDARD.

Unknown values become known as POSITIVE-NEGATIVE DEGREES PROGRESS from a STANDARD of comparison. Cold-hot could not be measured until 0° became a STANDARD(±) from which PROGRESSED POSITIVE-NEGATIVE DEGREES.

What applies in PRINCIPLE to the *individual* applies in PRINCIPLE to the *family, group, city, nation,* and *civilization,* i.e., the PROGRESSIVE RANGES of society. The PROGRESSIVE RANGE PRINCIPLE is MANIFESTED in any development or PROGRESSION, whether theological-philosophical-scientific.

Families UNITE under and are guided by parents who UNITE into *groups* under leaders, who UNITE into *nations* under a king, who UNITES his spiritual-mental-sensual nature and his *nation* under the spiritual guidance of his God.

Everyone is a ruled-ruler and all things INTE-

GRATE(+) to UNITY on PROGRESSIVE RANGES. DIS-INTEGRATE(—) the keystone from a PROGRESSIVE RANGE and the whole ENTITY DISINTEGRATES.

The *individual* needs something greater than himself to CAUSE *effort* to work, fight and die for and to give him a reason for being. His RANGE on the PROGRESSIVE RANGE MANIFESTS what that will be.

Love is a UNIversal, UNIFYING GOAL to give the *individual* a reason for being, to CAUSE and INTEGRATE his spiritual-mental-sensual *effort*, and to give him something to work, fight, and die for. The *individual* will work for sensual love GOALS; work and fight for intellectual love GOALS; and work, fight and die for the spiritual love GOALS of his *family, country* and *religion*.

The *individual* may MANIFEST *effort* to ACHIEVE personal GOALS, or GOALS of his *family, group, city, nation,* or *civilization*. Increasing GOAL *effort* on broader RANGES, in BALANCE, decreases GOAL *effort* on narrower RANGES. In ACHIEVING a major GOAL on the PROGRESSIVE RANGE, in BALANCE, the *individual* MANIFESTS less interest for minor GOALS on narrower RANGES.

The broader the RANGE of GOALS PROGRESSIVELY ACHIEVED the more mature and *civilized* is the *individual*. But the broader the RANGE of GOALS the broader the RANGE of *SELF-DISCIPLINED* responsibility, and the narrower the RANGE of *UNDISCIPLINED individual* freedom. In ACHIEVING(+) *civilization* GOALS, *family* GOALS are frustrated(—).

To go up-down the PROGRESSIVE RANGE by skipping RANGES is revolutionary and violent. Peaceful PROGRESS is the PROGRESSIVE ACHIEVEMENT of PROGRESSIVE RANGES and PROGRESSIVE DEGREES on the *SELF-DISCIPLINE* CYCLE.

When the *individual* narrows his RANGE of GOALS below the *individual* RANGE, or when he skips RANGES, he becomes maladjusted—or DERANGED. The DE-RANGED who strive for broad RANGE GOALS before narrower RANGE GOALS are ACHIEVED, have no narrow RANGE GOALS to JUDO to when broad RANGE GOALS are frustrated. So the *individual* DISINTEGRATES spiritually-mentally-physically.

The broader the GOAL RANGE the more *individuals* can be UNITED in common *effort* by a common GOAL. Common GOALS INTEGRATE the PROGRESSIVE RANGES of society; uncommon GOALS DISINTEGRATE. *Individualism* UNITES none; *families* UNITE more; politics UNITES *groups;* patriotism UNITES *nations;* religion UNITES *civilizations.*

Each RANGE of the PROGRESSIVE RANGE is composed of reactionary-conservative-radical *individuals.* Radicals(+) seek CHANGE to broader RANGES on a rising *civilization* and narrower RANGES in decline. Reactionaries(—) resist any CHANGE of RANGE. Conservatives(±) are CHANGEABLE in resisting CHANGE if NEGATIVE and assisting it if POSITIVE in value.

Each RANGE of the PROGRESSIVE RANGE has BALANCES within BALANCES of broader-narrower RANGES to form an INTEGRATED UNITY of BALANCES.

On the PROGRESSIVE RANGE of inferiority-average-superiority, the average(±) set STANDARDS when superiors(+) fail, and inferiors(—) set STANDARDS when the average fail. When kings fail to set STANDARDS, noblemen will; when noblemen fail, parents will; when parents fail, children will.

Inferiority-average-superiority is RELATIVE to the *individual's* RANGE on the PROGRESSIVE RANGE, to his DEGREE on the *SELF-DISCIPLINE* CYCLE, and to his RANGE on the DISTRIBUTION BALANCE. CHANGE of these DEGREES and RANGES is RELATIVE to the *individual.* Geniuses(+) can equalize down(—) to idiot

RANGE and DEGREE, but idiots(—) cannot equalize up(+) to genius RANGE and DEGREE.

The PROGRESSIVE RANGE of PERSPECTIVE MANIFESTS that the *individual* PERCEIVING close time-space, in BALANCE, loses PERSPECTIVE of distant time-space, i.e., the longer the time-space, in BALANCE, the broader the view.

PERCEIVE narrow RANGE facts, and in BALANCE, lose PERSPECTIVE of broad RANGE PRINCIPLES. On the PROGRESSIVE RANGE of PERSPECTIVE, narrow minded specialists have a narrow RANGE PERSPECTIVE; broad minded philosophers have a broad RANGE PERSPECTIVE; open minded wise men have a CHANGEABLE broad-narrow RANGE PERSPECTIVE.

Man, mind, and morals PROGRESS as facts UNIFY to concepts, and concepts UNIFY to PRINCIPLES, which UNIFY to UNIFIED PRINCIPLES. This is ACHIEVED only as the PERSPECTIVE PERCEPTION of knowledge and wisdom broadens.

Broad time-space contradicts the sensory experience of the living. Only old age and broad RANGE history can ACHIEVE the mental PERSPECTIVE PERCEPTION of such PRINCIPLES as the CYCLES, BALANCES, and PROGRESSIVE RANGES of man-nature.

The PROGRESSION of time-space on the PROGRESSIVE RANGES of man-nature, and in BALANCING CYCLES, MANIFESTS CUMULATION on the CAUSE-EFFECT BALANCE. Every action(+) has a BALANCING reaction(—) that CUMULATES reaction. CAUSE CUMULATES EFFECTS which are CAUSES to CUMULATE EFFECTS.

Any CHANGE CAUSES BALANCING CHANGES in a chain reaction of CHANGES. CUMULATION, like a tree, starts with a seed which PROGRESSIVELY CUMULATES major branches, minor branches, stems, and leaves.

"For want of a nail a shoe was lost; for want of a shoe a horse was lost; for want of a horse a battle was lost; for want of a battle a *nation* was lost." Minor CAUSES can CUMULATE major EFFECTS.

Repressed CUMULATIONS release violently. CUMULATE steam in a sealed pot and it explodes. Repress and CUMULATE emotions and it explosively releases in maniacal fury. Like the tea pot, release emotional steam as it CUMULATES to keep the *individual* whistling.

The PROGRESSION of CAUSE-EFFECT CUMULATION lies within POSITIVE-NEGATIVE LIMITS. Whether CUMULATING EFFECTS are POSITIVE-NEGATIVE is RELATIVE to the DEGREE and direction from a known STANDARD. POSITIVE action CUMULATES POSITIVE reactions; NEGATIVE actions CUMULATE NEGATIVE reaction—unless CHANGED by an opposing outside force or by *SELF-DISCIPLINED* effort.

The basis of *individual* effort is GOAL ACHIEVEMENT. Without a GOAL to UNIFY his spiritual-mental-physical *effort* the *individual* has no hope. No GOALS, no hope; no hope, no reason for being; no reason for being, no being.

The *individual* without a GOAL to drive to drives nowhere, but an *individual* with a GOAL is not easily led astray.

Survival-success-pleasure are basic GOALS sought by the *individual*. The wise *individual* strives for *survival* first, then *success*, and then *pleasure*, and may ACHIEVE all three. The fool seeks *pleasure* first and ACHIEVES nothing.

GOALS are RELATIVE to the reward-indifference-punishment BALANCING TRINITY. The promise of reward($+$) expresses GOAL *effort;* the fear of punishment($-$) represses GOAL *effort;* indifference($\pm$) distresses GOAL *effort.*

Reward CAUSES the exhibiting extrovert($+$); punishment CAUSES the inhibited introvert($-$); MODERATION CAUSES the CHANGEABLE ambivert($\pm$).

POSITIVE GOALS express($+$) spiritual-mental-physical *effort;* NEGATIVE GOALS depress($-$) *effort;* no GOALS repress($\pm$) *effort.*

How the *individual* uses *SELF-DISCIPLINED effort* to decide conflicts and to *succeed* over barriers and frustrations to ACHIEVE GOALS CAUSES his character and personality.

GOAL ACHIEVEMENT-conflict-frustration is CUMULATIVE. The more($+$) the *individual* ACHIEVES, the easier; the less($-$) he ACHIEVES, the more difficult. The strong($+$) attack($+$); the weak evade($\pm$); the lost retreat($-$). Will power is simply doing what the *individual* determines to do by *SELF-DISCIPLINED effort.*

Direct ACHIEVEMENT elates($+$); frustration deflates($-$); conflict confuses($\pm$). These are the basis of all emotions which are NEGATIVE-NEUTRAL-POSITIVE. Direct ACHIEVEMENT($+$) CAUSES POSITIVE emotions; indirect ACHIEVEMENT($\pm$) CAUSES NEUTRAL emotions; frustration($-$) CAUSES NEGATIVE emotions.

$1°$ ACHIEVEMENT $+$ $2°$ frustration $=$ $1°$ frustration; $3°$ ACHIEVEMENT $-$ $1°$ frustration $=$ $2°$ ACHIEVEMENT; $1°$ ACHIEVEMENT $-$ $1°$ frustration $=$ NEUTRAL or no CHANGE in ego, etc. The same PRINCIPLE applies to the spiritual-intellectual-material as well as to the mathematical.

JUDO is *SELF-DISCIPLINED* retreating before superior forces barring a GOAL, CAUSING the force to lose BALANCE and CONTROL. The JUDOIST retreats to PREPARED reserves and then counterattacks to ACHIEVE the BALANCE of CONTROL. Delicate bending reeds *survive* storms that shatter mighty unbending oaks.

GOAL activity and *effort* are SYMBOLIZED on this UNIFIED SYMBOL:

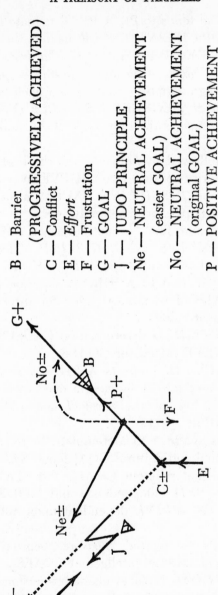

B — Barrier
     (PROGRESSIVELY ACHIEVED)
C — Conflict
E — *Effort*
F — Frustration
G — GOAL
J — JUDO PRINCIPLE
Ne — NEUTRAL ACHIEVEMENT
      (easier GOAL)
No — NEUTRAL ACHIEVEMENT
      (original GOAL)
P — POSITIVE ACHIEVEMENT

UNIFIED GOAL SYMBOL

The *individual* tends to PROGRESS-stagnate-REGRESS thru a *SELF-DISCIPLINE* CYCLE having the following PROGRESSIVE DEGREES: *Survival — hardship — SELF-DISCIPLINE — effort — success — leisure — pleasure — dissipation — degradation — ruin —* and back to *survival.*

In the *survival* DEGREE of the *SELF-DISCIPLINE* CYCLE, self-*survival* is the only law, GOAL and STANDARD.

Survival is followed by *hardship* and the brutal *DISCIPLINE* of authority seeking to ACHIEVE law and order. This *hardship* and *DISCIPLINE* CAUSES a stern, moral character which hopes for a better future.

The fear of and faith in authoritative *DISCIPLINE* CAUSES *individual SELF-DISCIPLINE.* This, INTEGRATED with faith and hope, CAUSES *SELF-DISCIPLINED* determination to ACHIEVE superior values, by sacrificing GOALS of temporary value for future GOALS of more permanent value.

SELF-DISCIPLINED determination CAUSES dynamic *efforts* to ACHIEVE hoped for GOALS.

SELF-DISCIPLINED efforts ACHIEVE *success.* This CAUSES pride and self confidence in one's own ability. It also CAUSES a loss of the *survival* and *DISCIPLINE* values that CAUSE *success.*

Success leads to *leisure* to contemplate the finer things of life. So intellectual and cultural GOALS and STANDARDS replace spiritual and religious GOALS and STANDARDS. *SELF-DISCIPLINED* independence and MODERATION replace *SELF-DISCIPLINE* dependent upon authoritarian *DISCIPLINE.*

Leisure leads to sensual *pleasure.* Sensual *pleasure* CAUSES a loss of spiritual-intellectual GOALS and values. Popularity as a GOAL replaces character-personality.

The *pleasure* DEGREE of the *SELF-DISCIPLINE* CYCLE leads to the *UNDISCIPLINED* excesses of *dissipation. SELF-DISCIPLINED* inhibitions are released to better experience the sensual and material *pleasures* of life.

Quantity replaces quality as a STANDARD of *pleasure* in this *dissipating* DEGREE of the *SELF-DISCIPLINE* CYCLE.

Dissipation degrades to degradation. Here the *individual* has perverted his *pleasures* by tasting all and the best, anything less CAUSES unhappiness. As the best gives no *pleasure,* the worst is sought.

Degradation degrades to *ruin.* Here all spiritual-intellectual-material values are DISINTEGRATED and *dissipated.* The *individual* loses his feeling of belonging to any RANGE of society, and having no GOALS, he has no reason for being. He has no moral-mental-physical strength to *survive* his *ruin.* Without a reason for being, he destroys himself, slowly by drugs and drink to make himself unconscious of reality, or quickly by suicide. Or he passes into the RANGE of subconscious delusion to live in an insane *world* of his own.

He crawls into the *survival* DEGREE of the *SELF-DIS-CIPLINE* CYCLE. But in the BALANCING CYCLES of God-man-nature, where nothing can be created nor destroyed, only CHANGED, the *dissipated* and *degraded* dead are replaced by the moral and *SELF-DISCIPLINED* living.

As the *individual* PROGRESSES-stagnates-REGRESSES on this SELF-DISCIPLINE CYCLE his STANDARDS and GOALS CHANGE from NEGATIVE to NEUTRAL to POSITIVE and back to NEGATIVE values.

As the *individual* CHANGES so CHANGES his art from spiritual to intellectual to sensual. Thus:

Rise (+)	*Peak* (±)	*Decline* (—)
Spiritual	Intellectual	Sensual
DISCIPLINE	*SELF-DISCIPLINED*	*UNDISCIPLINED*
Theology	Philosophy	Science
Deficiency	MODERATION	Excess
Reactionary	Conservative	Radical
Character	Personality	Popularity
NEGATIVE	NEUTRAL	POSITIVE

As MANIFESTED by this list, the *individual* rises with spiritual values, peaks with intellectual values, and declines with material values. He rises as a reactionary character, peaks as a conservative personality, and declines with radical popularity. He rises striving for superiority and declines striving for inferiority. Deficiency activates his rising GOAL *effort;* MODERATION stagnates it at the peak; and excess in decline *dissipates* GOAL *effort.*

As MANIFESTED by the BALANCE of values on the *SELF-DISCIPLINE* CYCLE, from the depths(—) of *survival* the *individual* rises(+) with NEGATIVE values; peaks(±) with NEUTRAL values, and declines(—) with POSITIVE values back to the depths(—) of *survival.*

The foregoing list MANIFESTS that NEGATIVE values are inconsistent in the POSITIVE column, i.e., there can be no theological scientist or reactionary radical. Thus, STANDARDS and GOALS on the rise of a *civilization* CYCLE are opposite and foreign to *civilizations* in decline.

Declining *civilizations* point with pride to their PROGRESS in material things as MANIFESTING their advancing *civilization.* They speak the truth, for as spiritual-intellectual values decrease, in BALANCE, material and sensual values increase. Such optimists in decline lack PERSPECTIVE of PRINCIPLES to PERCEIVE the whole TRINITY of truth.

The *SELF-DISCIPLINE* CYCLE PROGRESSES from narrow RANGES of PERSPECTIVE, GOALS, and society, to broader RANGES. It REGRESSES in reverse order. Rising *civilizations* broaden their RANGES; declining *civilizations* narrow their RANGES.

From self-*survival* GOALS the *individual* broadens his RANGE of PERSPECTIVE, GOALS, and society. He rises as he ACHIEVES his own GOALS first, then his *family, group, city, nation,* and *civilization.* He declines in reverse order.

The following SYMBOL INTEGRATES most UNIFIED

PRINCIPLE SYMBOLS into one UNIFIED PRINCIPLE SYMBOL. It can be used to explain most UNIFIED PRINCIPLES and activities of the *individual* on the *SELF-DISCIPLINE* CYCLES of the PROGRESSIVE RANGES of society.

The dates on the sides of the SYMBOL refer to paralleling Greek and Roman *civilizations*. These dates can be substituted by the *SELF-DISCIPLINE* CYCLE DEGREE dates of any *nation* or *civilization* which PROGRESSED-REGRESSED thru its complete CYCLE, i.e., was not eliminated by conquest. Their facts may differ but their PRINCIPLES are the same:

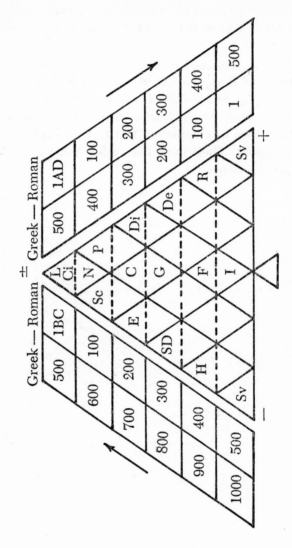

UNIFIED SYMBOL and *SELF-DISCIPLINE* CYCLE of *Civilization.*[1]

The *SELF-DISCIPLINE* CYCLE is composed of *individual* CYCLES INTEGRATED within *family* CYCLES, that INTEGRATE with *group* CYCLES, and so on up the PROGRESSIVE RANGES of society, to form the INTEGRATED UNITY of a *civilization SELF-DISCIPLINE* CYCLE.

Civilization SELF-DISCIPLINE CYCLES are INTEGRATED within a *world* CYCLE. As one *civilization* ACHIEVES its peak of *leisure* and begins a decline, another *civilization* CYCLE begins rising from its depths of *survival* conditions. The thousand-year CYCLES of *civilization* are SYMBOLIZED:

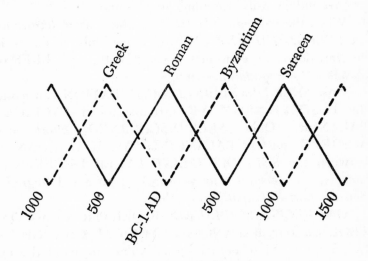

1000-year *Civilization* CYCLES

Legend for Illustration on Page 278

1. Sv—Survival	L—Leisure	I—Individual
H—Hardship	P—Pleasure	F—Family
SD—Self-discipline	Di—Dissipation	G—Group
E—Effort	De—Degradation	C—City
S—Success	R—Ruin	N—Nation
		Ci—Civilization

It is predetermined that the *individual's* destiny is determined RELATIVE to his own self-determination. CYCLICAL BALANCES and PROGRESSIVE RANGES are his predetermined destiny. If he cannot stop these, he can self-determine their DEGREE of CHANGE.

The *individual* cannot stop the sleep-awake CYCLICAL BALANCE, but he can CONTROL its DEGREE of CHANGE to avoid excess-deficiency. He can CONTROL his CYCLICAL BALANCES to ACHIEVE the greatest DEGREE of rhythmic harmony within the INTEGRATED UNITY of other CYCLICAL BALANCES and RANGES. It is the difference between happily dancing in rhythm with a partner and clumsily stumbling all over him.

When the *individual* ACHIEVES the peak of *leisure* on the *SELF-DISCIPLINE* CYCLE, he can only go down. If he goes down, he continues down thru the DEGREES of *dissipation—degradation—ruin.*

Only *SELF-DISCIPLINED* MODERATION can avoid the POSITIVE-NEGATIVE extremes of a CYCLICAL BALANCE. Only *SELF-DISCIPLINED* *effort* can ACHIEVE constant BALANCING CYCLICAL CHANGE between the *SELF-DISCIPLINE* CYCLE DEGREES of *success*($-$)*—leisure*($\pm$)*—pleasure*($+$) to avoid *degradation* to *effort—dissipation* or below.

Only *SELF-DISCIPLINED* MODERATION can CONTROL constant BALANCING CYCLICAL CHANGE between spiritual-intellectual-sensual values to avoid the excess-deficiency of any of these values.

The thousand-year *SELF-DISCIPLINE* CYCLE of *civilization* is predetermined to repeat itself unless CONTROLLED by *SELF-DISCIPLINED* *effort* and MODERATION between spiritual-intellectual-sensual values.

In conclusion: Mathematics cannot be applied without the mathematical key words "plus" and "minus," or their SYMBOLS ($+$) ($-$), for all mathematical problems are based on them. Wisdom cannot be applied without UNI-

FIED PRINCIPLE key words, for all wisdom is based on them.

INTEGRATIONS of mathematical PRINCIPLES simplify the most complex mathematical problems. INTEGRATIONS of UNIFIED PRINCIPLES simplify the most complex life problems.

UNIFIED PRINCIPLES enable the wisdom of judgment to PERCEIVE values, not as right or wrong, but as right-wrong in DEGREE. Right-wrong, being opposite sides of the same STANDARD, UNIFIED PRINCIPLES enable judgments by CHANGEABLE DEGREE, not UNCHANGING law.

UNIFIED PRINCIPLES enable judgments to be RELATIVE to all the laws EFFECTING the PROGRESSIVE RANGES of society: Moral law is common to and INTEGRATES all; ethical law is common to many; legal law is common to less; *individual* law is common to none and DISINTEGRATES the PROGRESSIVE RANGES of society.

Some truths can only be believed, reasoned, or PERCEIVED. On the other hand, the whole TRINITY of truth has NEGATIVE-NEUTRAL-POSITIVE values that can only be believed-reasoned-PERCEIVED in INTEGRATED UNITY.

Beyond material physics is mental logic; beyond this is spiritual metaphysics. The materialistic scientist sees thru sensory feeling; the intellectual philosopher reasons thru mental logic; the spiritualistic mystic believes thru the souls' revelation. Each has parts of the TRINITY of truth but not the whole. Only UNIFIED PRINCIPLES enable this INTEGRATED UNITY.

Spiritual-intellectual-sensual truth can be ACHIEVED, but only one at a time. The *individual* is a spiritual-intellectual-sensual TRINITY, but he cannot be a mystic-philosopher-scientist at the same time. Only UNIFIED PRINCIPLES can ACHIEVE the INTEGRATION to MANIFEST the UNITY of the TRINITY of knowledge and wisdom.

Without PRINCIPLES to guide him, the *individual* does not know where he's been, where he's going, or when he goes astray. PRINCIPLES are the guide to truth, for only PRINCIPLES MANIFEST truth as a CHANGING-UN-CHANGING TRINITY of NEGATIVE-NEUTRAL-POSI-TIVE values.

Knowledge of UNIFIED PRINCIPLES is good-evil RELATIVE to the DEGREE of wisdom CONTROLLING it—between POSITIVE-NEGATIVE LIMITS and broad-narrow RANGES.

Date Due

		PRINTED IN U. S. A.	